CW00554556

Wire rope grip termir

Performance tests on wire rope terminatio.. ....g wire rope grips and some comparisons with alternative designs

C H H Corden

CONTENTS

SYNOPSIS

Following four major incidents in which the failure of wire rope terminations made using wire rope grips occurred the Research & Laboratory Services Division (RLSD) of the Health & Safety Executive (HSE), now renamed the Health and Safety Laboratory (HSL), began a programme of tests to investigate the efficiencies of such terminations. Over 650 tests were carried out, mainly using BS 462 grips but small numbers of tests were also made using Crosby, DIN 1142, Fist, Iron and Eureka grips for comparison purposes.

A test method was evolved in which a computer was used to load the terminations in increments and to automatically measure and record any slip of the rope in the terminations. Using this system it was possible to detect very small movements (microslip) at a much earlier stage, and lower load, than slip detected visually. Such microslip measurements proved more reliable and less variable than the measurement of visible slip. Instrument detected microslip usually occurred at loads less than half those at which the slip was detected visually so the efficiencies quoted in this report, which are based on the microslip initiation loads, are well below efficiencies based on visible slip given in literature and Standards for this type of termination.

The majority of the tests using BS 462 grips were made using the 16 mm size. Tests included galvanised and ungalvanised grips, tightening the grips to different torque values, and varying the numbers of grips in the terminations. The results showed that terminations made using the minimum number of galvanised grips recommended in BS 462 (editions 1958, 1969 and 1983) and practical torque values, gave efficiencies of less than 30% generally. These tests showed how extra grips can be used to increase the efficiencies at practical torque values.

The tests also covered a range of BS 462 grips from 9mm to 19mm. The results suggested that generally the smaller sizes were more efficient than the larger ones. The programme included tests using four different rope constructions which showed that those with steel cores produced higher termination efficiencies than those with fibre cores.

A number of comparison tests were made with some of the alternative designs of grip commercially available. These tests were restricted to the 16mm size. In some cases grip manufacturers publish recommended torque values for their grips but in several cases these seemed unrealistically high for application under many service conditions unless power tools and other special pieces of equipment to hold the termination are available. With some designs of grip the use of high torques can also damage the rope. When more practical torques were used the termination efficiencies generally dropped dramatically. Only the DIN 1142 grip had a recommended tightening torque, 49 Nm (36 lbf.ft) for the 16 mm size, that was both practical to apply and which with the appropriate number of grips gave efficiencies around the 80% value usually quoted for this type of termination. Many of the other grips of the same size when torqued to similar practical values gave termination efficiencies, based on microslip measurements, in the range 10% to 30%.

The report illustrates the rapid loss of torque with time, up to 40% overnight when the grips were left on an unloaded fibre cored rope, and after the application of a load. The results showed the need for more frequent re-torquing than is often practised if the termination efficiency is to be maintained at an acceptable level. The tests also illustrated the value of greasing the bolt threads before use, and in the case of BS 462 grips the large differences in the performance of galvanised and ungalvanised grips.

The tests described in this paper were all carried out in the 1980s. The findings were presented to BSI at that time and these eventually led to the withdrawal of BS 462 in May 1992. Large numbers of these grips are still in use however and will be for many years to come so it is felt that a wider publication of the results through this paper is useful in that it should help users to understand the performance of the grips in more detail and help them in planning maintenance schedules more knowledgeably.

PART 1

Part 1 of this paper covers the method used to test terminations made using wire rope grips. Observations made about the quality of BS 462 grips and features which affect their performance in service are discussed. This part concludes with a discussion of the results of tests in the first phase of the programme in which the numbers of grips and the torques applied to them were investigated.

It should be noted that as a result of the research reported in this paper BS 462 was eventually withdrawn in 1991. Large numbers of grips purporting to have been made to BS 462 remain in service however and will continue to be used for many years.

INTRODUCTION

In the last fifteen years the Research and Laboratory Services Division (RLSD) of the Health and Safety Executive, now renamed the Health and Safety Laboratory (HSL), has investigated three incidents in which the failure of rope terminations made with wire rope grips led to fatalities or serious injuries, i.e. Humber Bridge construction incident, Piper-Tharos offshore platform gangway collapse, and an Exmouth hotel lift failure. In a fourth incident all four wire rope terminations on the counterweight side of a four rope lift installation in an office block in Nottingham failed. In all four incidents the strength, or slip load, of the wire rope termination was the prime factor causing the failure of the termination though in two cases failure of the terminations occurred as secondary events after failures or malfunctions in other parts of the operating systems. The investigations showed that the efficiencies of the terminations, based on the Minimum Breaking Loads (MBL) of the ropes, were very much lower than the figure of 80% often quoted in literature e.g. BS 462:1983 (until amended in 1985). In practice it appeared that efficiencies of around 20% to 30% were more realistic, and even lower figures around 10% were possible in some circumstances. The situation was complicated by the absence from BS 462 of any recommended torque values to which the nuts on the grips should be initially tightened and the absence of published fitting instructions by the grip manufacturers. These RLSD investigations indicated that the minimum numbers of grips for terminations on different sized ropes, as recommended in BS 462:1958, 1969, and 1983 (until Appendix A was amended), were insufficient if 80% efficiencies were to be achieved. In some cases the manufacturers of alternative types of grip to the BS 462 design, do publish tables showing the minimum numbers of grips for terminations on different sizes of rope and a recommended torque value for each size. In the opinion of the author some of these torque values seem generally too high to achieve in practice under field conditions unless special equipment is available to hold the rope and to apply the torque.

HSE/RLSD decided to investigate the slippage of wire rope grips under the general programme heading "Factors contributing to the premature failure of wire ropes and their terminations", it having been agreed that in the first place any research would concentrate on the BS 462 grips. The testing of BS 462 grips began in April 1984 under a programme titled "Determination of the strength of wire rope terminations made with BS 462 wire rope grips". Initial results of this research led to the amendment of BS 462:1983 Appendix A in 1985 and the publication of an HSE Press Release covering the need for this amendment. As a consequence of this programme serious doubt has been expressed about the performance of the BS 462 grips and the unlikelihood of their meeting the 80% efficiency criteria without radical redesign or vast improvements being made in the quality of the grips commercially available at the start of this programme. Before any effort was made to re-design the existing BS 462 grip it was considered advisable that the main alternative designs of wire rope grips available in the UK should also be subjected to identical tests on the same laboratory equipment.

This paper summarises the results from over 650 tests on individual terminations carried out between April 1984 and February 1988. Most of these were made using BS 462 grips but a small number of tests were also carried out on Crosby,

DIN 1142, Fist, Iron, and Eureka grips for comparison purposes on a limited scale.

Since this work was completed BS 462 has been withdrawn but there are large numbers of grips still in use which purport to have been made to this standard. It is hoped that publication of the results of this research will give grip users some insight into the performance of terminations made with this type of grip under static load conditions.

TEST PROGRAMME

The basic programme was initially split into several separate phases so that progress could be more easily monitored. Some of the planned work in phase 2 on the loss of torque with time and the effects of re-torquing in service, and the work on worn grips in phase 5, was curtailed and later abandoned in the light of the findings from the phases 1 and 6 of the work.

The initial programme for the BS 462 grips was as follows:

PHASE 1 - Aim: To show the effects of different tightening torques and different numbers of grips on the slip load, or efficiency, of the termination.

PHASE 2 - Aim: To investigate the loss of torque with time, the effects of load cycling, and the effects of re-torquing.

PHASE 3 - Aim: To show the effect of different rope constructions on the slip load of the termination.

PHASE 4 - Aim: To investigate the effect of rope size on the slip load of the termination.

PHASE 5 - Aim: To show the effect of using grips with worn bridges on the slip load of the termination.

PHASE 6 - Aim: To compare the performance of some of the alternative designs of rope grip with that of grips to BS 462.

METHOD OF TESTING

Experience has shown that tests on wire ropes and their end fittings often produce a very wide scatter in the results. There are many reasons for this but important factors include variations in the quality and performance of individual fittings, manufacturing variations in the ropes themselves, and variations in the preparation of the test specimens and in carrying out the tests. In order to try to reduce the scatter of the results as much as possible a standard method of testing was established. Details of this method are described in the following section.

All the different sizes and constructions of ropes used in the programme were purchased in single lengths in order to try to avoid manufacturing variations which can occur between different batches of rope. Although all the test samples of a given size and construction can be cut from these single lengths there could still be some minor variations which have arisen during the manufacture of long lengths of rope.

The BS 462 grips were purchased in a number of batches from three different suppliers to try to give a more balanced picture of the quality of those being marketed. These different batches did reveal some manufacturing variations, e.g. in the surface finish and the quality of the zinc coating on the galvanised grips, but the size of the main programme prevented these aspects being examined in more detail. The biggest single variant, even between grips from the same batch, was the angle between the U bolt legs, almost none were truly parallel. In view of these observations and to try to reduce the effects of such manufacturing variations on the test results as much as possible, wherever practical all the grips used in a particular phase were taken from a single batch purchased from one supplier.

New grips were used for each test but they were not specially selected for straightness or quality. Grips were only rejected if during tightening up there was any sign that the threads had stripped or had begun to yield abnormally.

In preliminary tests to establish the test procedure some of the U bolt threads were lightly greased before the grips were assembled on the rope. This reduced the frictional losses and gave slightly higher termination efficiencies than those tests where the grips were used as supplied with no extra grease. However when several users of this type of termination were questioned they all stated that in practice this type of grip was normally fitted as supplied. It was rare for any grease to be put on the threads before use. The majority of the tests with BS 462 grips were therefore made with the grips as supplied i.e. no additional grease was put on the threads, as this gave the more realistic normal use conditions.

In all the tests however a smear of grease was put on the face of each nut which contacted the bridge piece. This was done in order to reduce friction between the nut and the bridge piece when measuring the torque. Without this grease the torque tended to increase in sudden uncontrollable steps due to the difference between the coefficients of static and kinetic friction, "stiction effects", making it very difficult to apply or measure a specific value. With a little grease on the face of each nut the stiction effects were greatly reduced and the torque being applied could be better controlled. This action was also carried out on the alternative grip designs tested, where appropriate.

All the test specimens were made up with the grips spaced at 6d intervals (where d = diameter of the rope) as recommended in BS 462 (Fig.1). The first grip was placed as close as practical to the thimble points without causing excessive distortion in the rope. Tests on different spacings between the grips were not included in this programme. The non-test end of each sample was terminated with a conical capping (Fig.1) or a number of closely spaced grips (Fig.2). The use of closely spaced grips is never recommended in service, here it was only used to save time and space in those tests where only small loads were to be applied.

A new BS 464 ordinary thimble was used for each test.

To measure rope slip in the termination a reference plate mounted on a special rope clamp was fitted to the tail end of the rope (Figs 2 and 3). Movement of this reference plate relative to the fixed base of the test machine was measured by means of a linear displacement transducer mounted on the end of a steel bar. When a load was applied to a termination the two parts of the rope both stretched elastically as the load was shared between them. This stretching of the ropes caused the reference plate to move away from the fixed end of the machine i.e. away from the thimble end of the termination. When slip of the rope through the grips occurred this plate moved in the opposite direction, towards the thimble end i.e. the tail part of the termination began to shorten.

The instrumentation used was capable of detecting displacements of 0.0025 mm. For the purposes of this programme any shortening of the tail part of the termination by 0.015 mm or more was called slip, or microslip. The actual figure used was not critical, it was chosen so that such movement would generate sufficient change in voltage to trigger the slip detection and recording system into operation. The use of a round steel bar, positioned alongside the test specimen (Fig.2), to attach the displacement transducer to the fixed lower crosshead on the test rig effectively compensated for changes in the length of the test specimen with variations in the temperature of the laboratory during each test.

Movement of the order of that defined as slip (i.e. 0.015 mm or more), once initiated in these tests was shown to be continuous over many hours. The rate of slip was very slow however, much too slow to observe by eye without special instrumentation. From the point of view of comparing test results the slip initiation point is much easier to identify than the point at which the rate of slip reaches some chosen higher value. Many tests in other laboratories in the past have relied on visible slip - a rather undefinable quantity which occurs at much higher loads than those measured in these tests. Preliminary tests indicated that the slip initiation point as measured in these tests occurred at loads less than half those at which most observers would have first detected visible slip in the same termination. The loads at which visible slip was detected also showed very wide variations between repeated tests with the same observer, and between different observers viewing the same test.

Whilst fitting each specimen into the testing machine a bush was fitted inside each thimble to reduce the distortion of the thimble during the test. If this was not done then the elongation of the thimble caused a movement of the reference plate on the tail rope of the termination away from the thimble end of the specimen. This hid the earliest slip movement of the rope which caused the reference plate to move towards the thimble. Without a bush in the thimble the amount of distortion also varied with the load applied to the rope and with manufacturing variations between individual thimbles. By preventing the distortion of the main body of the thimble, and consequently the overriding of the thimble points, the scatter of the results at each point in this programme was appreciably reduced.

In the case of the BS 462 grips, for which the grip manufacturers do not publish recommended torques, tests were carried out at several torque values to establish performance curves. In the case of the alternative designs tests were carried out at the recommended torques. Where these recommended torque values seemed, in the opinion of the author, excessively high and not practical to apply under service conditions without the use of specialised ancilliary eqipment, some tests were also carried out at lower torques.

In each test all the test grips were torqued up to the same selected value. The grip furthest from the thimble was not tightened up to a torque lower than the others as recommended in BS 462 for to do so would have introduced another variable. The statement in BS 462 would be valid if high torques were applied for it would reduce the damage to the wires under this grip, where the majority of the breakages in this programme occurred, but it would also weaken the termination producing a lower termination efficiency. BS 462 gives no indication of how much less torque to apply to this grip. The loss of torque with time and after the application of a load, discussed later in this paper, would further complicate the situation.

The grips were torqued up immediately prior to the start of the test whilst a small tensile load of between 1 kN and 3 kN was applied to the rope. The two nuts on each grip were tightened progressively and alternatively to maintain the correct alignment of the bridge to the U bolt. When all the nuts on all the grips had been tightened once to the required value they were rechecked, and retightened if necessary, before starting a test, in case there had been any interaction from the tightening of adjacent grips. In the majority of the tests the grips were not retightened after a higher load, say the maximum Safe Working Load, had been applied, even though in many cases under service conditions the nuts would be retightened once the normal service static load had been hung on the rope. The reason for this was that there are some situations where this cannot be done and it was considered desirable to test the grip terminations under the worst conditions likely to be met in service.

The load was applied, under computer control, in increments up to the point at which slip was initiated. Both the load and the movement of the reference plate were recorded automatically at fixed intervals throughout each test. In the early part of each test the load was applied in steps of 10 kN at 5 min intervals. When the load reached a value about 20 kN below that at which slip initiation was expected the load increments were reduced to 5 kN and the time intervals increased to 10 min. This increase in the hold period and reduction of the load steps was made in the light of experience gained in the preliminary tests. In these tests it was found that slip did not normally commence the instant the load was increased but usually only after the higher load had been held for about 4 to 5 minutes. When slip was detected the load was held automatically for 15 min to ensure that the slip was continuous. The load was then reduced to zero and immediately reapplied to the previous maximum value to check that slip recommenced at the same load. If slip did not occur on the second cycle at the same load then the load was increased in 5 kN steps until it recommenced. In practice in over 99% of the tests slip occurred during this second cycle at exactly the same load as in the first load cycle.

If any wires broke during a test then the test was stopped and the maximum load applied recorded. This value was recorded on the graphs with a different symbol but it was taken as the equivalent point to the slip initiation point because once slip or wire breaks occurred then there must be some doubt about the continued integrity of the termination.

Termination efficiencies mentioned in this report are all based on the Minimum Breaking Load (MBL) of the rope (i.e. the value normally given in the appropriate Standard) not its Actual Breaking Load i.e.

$$\text{Termination Efficiency} = \frac{\text{Slip initiation load}}{\text{MBL of rope}} \times 100\%$$

where the slip initiation load is the load being applied at the moment when microslip movement is first detected. If the actual breaking loads of the ropes had been used the efficiencies would have been lower.

It had been planned originally to test grips on both galvanised and ungalvanised ropes of the same constructions but this would have appreciably extended the test programme. As the thickness of the zinc layer on drawn galvanised wires is very thin it was the opinion of the author that any effect on the termination efficiency would not have been significant and it would have been lost within the normal scatter of the results. In practice only one of the ropes used in these tests was galvanised. It should be noted however from a general corrosion protection point of view that galvanised fittings should always be used on a galvanised rope.

GENERAL OBSERVATIONS

All the BS 462 grips purchased for use in this programme had been stamped "BSS" and with a rope size e.g. "5/8". Checking the dimensions of the grips revealed that all the grips had been made to the dimensions given in BS 462:Part 1:1958. This Standard was withdrawn in 1971, being replaced by BS 462:Part 2:1969. The 1969 Standard was replaced by BS 462:1983. As a consequence it was found that in most cases the diameters of the U bolt legs were well undersize according to the 1969 and 1983 Standards e.g. 9mm...-19%, 13 mm...-23%, 16 mm...-4% to -10%, 19 mm...-22%. Where several batches of grips had been bought in one size e.g. 16 mm, there was some variation between the different batches. The U bolt legs in all the 19 mm grips were of the same nominal diameter as those in the 16 mm grips - a legacy from the earlier 1958 Standard. The thickness of the bridge pieces also varied between batches, many being 10% or more undersize by the 1969 and 1983 Standards but being fairly close to the 1958 dimensions. Some of the bridges had excessively large holes for the U bolt legs but these hole dimensions are not specified in detail in either the 1958 or 1969 Standards. The overall height of a small proportion of the U bolts were well outside the specified dimensional tolerances given in all three editions of the Standard, some being undersize by up to

7

about 10% whilst others were oversize by a similar amount against the two earlier Standards. It should be noted that the test programme was begun in 1984, and most of the grips were purchased in the period 1984 to 1986, so it was not expected that the grips would meet all the requirements of the then recently published 1983 Standard. In practice none of the BS 462 grips purchased for this programme met either the 1969 or the 1983 dimensional specifications.

If grips complying with the dimensional requirements of BS 462:1983 had been available for this programme it is estimated that although the grips themselves should have been slightly stronger the termination efficiencies would not have been appreciably altered unless the grips had been made to a very much higher manufacturing standard.

Almost every one of the BS 462 grips had the legs of their U bolts splayed out due to poor manufacture with the result that the faces of the nuts were not parallel with the bases of the bridge pieces. Alignment errors between U bolt legs were generally about 5 deg but errors of 10 deg or even larger were found. By contrast the U bolt legs of DIN 1142 grips, tested in Phase 6 of the programme, were all within approximately 1 deg of parallel. On tightening up the nuts on the BS 462 grips the nuts initially made contact with the bridge pieces only on one side (Fig.4). Further tightening caused the corners of the nuts to dig into the galvanising on the bridge pieces absorbing an appreciable proportion of the applied torque, and thereby affecting the efficiency of the termination. Some torque was also absorbed because the misaligned U bolts caused the bridge piece to bend slightly. The use of loose washers under the nuts was tried in some of the preliminary tests, to see if they would reduced this digging-in effect, but they seemed to have little effect.

Some of the smallest of the U bolts showed manufacturing damage in the form of a sharp deep Vee notch on one leg where they had been held whilst being bent into the U shape. Others had several damaged turns at the end of the thread on the other leg. The notches could form a point of weakness, especially under fatigue conditions, though none failed at this point in this test programme. The damaged turns could prevent the nuts being tightened effectively.

The 'across-flats' dimensions of the nuts on some grips were different from others on the same nominal size of grip. This was most noticeable on the 16 mm and 19 mm grips where two socket sizes were required for each size of grip to ensure that all the nuts could be tightened.

The threaded length of the U bolt legs varied appreciably not only between different grips but also in many cases between the two legs on the same grip. In a few cases when the grips had been tightened up in a termination the ends of the nuts were found to lie within about three turns of the end of the thread on the U bolt legs i.e. almost within the run-out region at the end of the thread and in the area where in some cases several turns had been damaged when the U bolts were being bent into shape. The overall heights of the U bolts of 16 mm grips were found to vary from about 67 mm to 81 mm, a small proportion of these being well outside the tolerance specified in any of the three editions of BS 462. Other sizes of grip showed similar proportional variations in the overall height and in the length of the screwed legs but individual dimensions were not recorded. In order to use a torque meter on the grips it was necessary to purchase extra long sockets because generally the length of the U bolt thread protruding through the nuts during tightening prevented a normal length socket from fully engaging the nut.

Although no table of recommended torques for different sizes of BS 462 grips has been published by the grip manufacturers, a table of torques based on 70% of the theoretical Yield stress of the U bolt legs has been calculated, but not published, by independent researchers for RLSD, e.g. this table gives a torque of 53 lbf.ft (72 Nm) for 16 mm BS 462 grips. Torque values were also published by the Technical Services Department of British Ropes Ltd in 1973 (Ref. Technical Information Sheet "Fitting of Bull Dog grips" 1502/73). This document gives higher torques values than those calculated for RLSD, e.g. a torque of 80 lbf.ft (108 Nm) for 16 mm BS 462:1958 grips. Both these sets of calculated values proved to be excessively high in practice for they caused appreciable damage to the ropes under each grip. With 16 mm BS 462 grips the maximum torque from a damage limitation point of view, as determined by experienced grip fitters from commercial organisations, was in the range 30 - 35 lbf.ft (41 - 47 Nm).

During the tests on galvanised 16 mm BS 462 grips it was found that torques in the range 60 to 80 lbf.ft (81 to 108 Nm) occasionally caused the threads on the U bolts to strip. In one case the threads stripped at only 30 lbf.ft (41 Nm) torque. In every case where the threads stripped only the tips of the threads were damaged. The general looseness of the nuts on the U bolts indicated that the problem was caused by excessive manufacturing clearance tolerances allowed between the threads of the nuts and those on the U bolts presumably to accommodate zinc coatings of variable thicknesses. The same problem was not found on the ungalvanised grips where the nuts and the U bolt threads were generally a closer fit.

During this programme it was noted on many occasions that even after the initiation of slip the rate of slip varied very slightly from moment to moment. This was probably as a result of individual wires on the strand crowns passing under the hoop of each grip, or passing strand crown wires in the other part of the rope where the two parts were pressed together under the grips.

The effects of increasing the load were also not instantaneous. Generally slip was first detected after a pause of four to five minutes after an increased load had been applied. This delay was presumably related to creep effects within the rope as the main core and the strands continued to distort for several minutes after the application of the load increment. To overcome the effects of this delay each load increment near the expected slip initiation load was held for 10 min.

When wire breaks occurred at the test termination end of the sample they were always under a grip and on the live (or load carrying) part of the rope, either on a strand crown where the wire had been nicked by pressure from a wire on a strand crown on the tail side, or where severe nicking had occurred due to pressure between adjacent strands in the same part of the rope. In the whole test programme no breaks occurred where the rope touched either the hoop of the U bolt or the bridge of the grip. The vast majority of the breaks were under the grip furthest from the thimble, the remainder were under the grip next to the furthest from the thimble. No breaks occurred under the grip next to the thimble. This distribution of the breaks is as expected for under the grip furthest from the thimble the whole of the load is carried by the live part of the rope. Between the furthest grip and the grip next to it some of the load is transferred to the rope on the tail side of the termination so the stresses in the live part are reduced.

Terminations made using BS 462 grips were generally not capable of holding loads up to the actual breaking loads of the ropes. In a few cases loads up to the MBL of the rope were reached but in the vast majority of the cases where high loads were applied individual wires began to break when the load was raised beyond about 85% of the MBL, e.g. with a 16 mm diameter rope with a MBL of 150 kN, and an actual measured breaking load of 162 kN, wires began to break when the applied load exceeded about 130 kN. Similar results were obtained with ropes of other sizes and other constructions.

Test specimens made with fibre cored ropes which were torqued up and left unloaded were found to lose up to about 40% of the original torque overnight. With steel cored ropes the overnight loss of torque was a little less. The loss was due to the bedding-down of the strands under the individual grips.

Ropes with fibre main cores showed a lot of damage to the fibre cores under the positions of the grips after high torques had been applied to the nuts. This damage was expected where loads above the normal safe working loads for the ropes had been applied because the fibre cores could withstand less stretching than the wire strands. However checks on ropes under grips which had been torqued up under no load conditions revealed that at the higher torques used in some of the tests the fibre cores were being severely damaged, or even chopped apart, simply by the pressure exerted by the crushed strands. For fibre cored ropes therefore the highest of the torque levels used in these tests would not be usable in practice. Core chopping with a 16 mm dia 6x36 FC rope began at torques of about 70 lbf.ft (95 Nm) with no load applied to the termination. When a load equal to the Safe Working Load (SWL) for the rope was applied severe core damage occurred at torques over about 50 lbf.ft (68 Nm). This latter value was confirmed by observations made by an experienced and competent person who regularly fitted this type of termination to ropes in service.

In the whole of this programme the tests were stopped when the instrumentation indicated slip as defined earlier. Because the slip initiation points were generally well below the 80% efficiency quoted in literature for this type of termination one or two tests were extended until the slip became visible to the naked eye without the aid of any instrumentation. In general to reach this point the load had to be increased until it was approximately double the slip initiation load measured by the instrumentation. The rate of slip at the stage when it became easily visible was such that the termination would fail totally within a few minutes. Visible slip observations produced wide variations in the loads at which different persons were able to detect the first visible movement. Repeated tests with the same test parameters and under the same conditions using the same observer also resulted in a very wide scatter in the results.

RESULTS AND DISCUSSION OF TESTS

PHASE 1 - The effects of Torque and Number of Grips

The aim of the first part of the programme was to show the effects of different tightening torques and different numbers of grips on the slip load, or efficiency, of the termination.

All the tests in this part of the programme were carried out on a 16 mm diameter 6x36(14/7and7/7/1)FC ungalvanised rope. All the grips were new. In the first tests all the grips and thimbles were galvanised. They were used as supplied i.e. without washers under the nuts to prevent the corners of the nuts gouging into the galvanised coating on the bridges, and without any grease put on the threads of the U bolts or nuts before assembly on the rope.

In the second part of this phase similar tests were made using ungalvanised grips and thimbles.

A total of 214 tests were carried out. The results obtained in the individual tests using 3, 4, 5, and 6 galvanised grips and a galvanised thimble, and 3, 4, and 5 ungalvanised grips and an ungalvanised thimble, in each termination are illustrated in the Appendix to this part of the paper. The results are summarised in Fig.5 and Fig.6 and combined together on Fig.7.

The individual test points where the instrumentation detected slip in each termination are shown on the figures in the Appendix as dots. Points marked with small circles "o" represent the loads reached in tests which were stopped after one or more wires had broken. In a few tests complete breakage of the rope occurred usually at the non-test end of the sample. It should be noted that the test termination had not failed in any way at these loads, which are marked on the graphs by "*". The best fit straight line was calculated using a statistical linear regression method. This straight line is shown on each figure.

For clarity on the graphs where more than one test gave the same slip load the individual tests results have been plotted slightly displaced to the left or right of the nominal torque value used e.g on Fig A1.1 five tests were carried out with a torque of 20 lbf.ft (27 Nm) and these gave slip loads of 20, 15, 15, 15, and 15 kN respectively. For clarity on the torque axis of each graph the actual torque values used have been circled.

With a termination made using three galvanised grips, the minimum number originally recommended for a 16 mm diameter rope in BS 462:1958, 1969, and 1983:Appendix A (before its amendment in 1985), termination efficiencies from the tests ranged from approximately 10% at 20 lbf.ft (27 Nm) to approximately 50% at 80 lbf.ft (108 Nm). However the use of torques towards the upper end of this range is not really practical in many applications because it becomes impossible to hold the rope and grip whilst applying the torque without a vice or some other special equipment.

In practice it was found that the maximum torque which could be applied on the 16 mm grips, using a spanner or an adjustable wrench of reasonable size, was about 35 lbf.ft (47 Nm) when the rope was being held by hand, and about 50 lbf.ft (68 Nm) when the grip was being held in a vice. However at torques of about 50 lbf.ft (68 Nm) on 16 mm grips the rope under the hoops of the U bolts showed appreciable indentations, damaging the rope and deep enough to be of concern.

Trials carried out with the help of a small number of professionally trained and experienced grip fitters, who worked for commercial wire rope servicing companies, indicated, in their opinion, that the limit for acceptable indentations in the tail rope was reached with 16 mm grips when torques of about 30 - 35 lbf.ft (41 - 47 Nm) were applied. Torquing up would stop at the point, based on their previous experience and training, where the indentation, or damage, in the rope reached a certain level judged by eye. If their experience of how much torque to apply in practice is accepted then the tests in this programme indicate that the initial termination efficiency, when using three galvanised grips on a 16 mm rope, may be only about 15% - 20%.

Another practical problem experienced during this programme was that trying to apply torques in the range 60 to 80 lbf.ft (81 to 108 Nm) sometimes caused the threads on the galvanised U bolts to strip. In the worst case the thread on one U bolt leg stripped at only 30 lbf.ft (41 Nm) torque.

High torques also caused damage to the fibre cores of the ropes.

Increasing the numbers of galvanised grips raised the efficiency of the terminations but even with 6 grips at 30 lbf.ft (41 Nm) torque the efficiency was only of the order of 43% (Fig.5). To reach the 80% efficiency level often quoted in literature for this type of termination using six grips required torques of about 50 lbf.ft (68 Nm).

Tests using ungalvanised grips and thimbles gave appreciably higher slip loads than the corresponding tests using galvanised components (Figs.6 & 7). Three grips at 30 lbf.ft (41 Nm) torque gave efficiencies of about 37%. Five grips at the same torque gave efficiencies of about 73%. Six grips at 30 lbf.ft (41 Nm), although not tested in this programme, would probably have given efficiencies of 80% or more.

Comparing the galvanised and ungalvanised grips it appeared that with galvanised components more torque is lost in friction in the threads. With the ungalvanised threads the manufacturing tolerances on the U bolt and nut threads gave a better fit and this produced a stronger joint. It was also noted that the thread surfaces of the ungalvanised grips were both smoother and more consistent than those of the galvanised grips.

Although ungalvanised thimbles were used with the ungalvanised grips such thimbles are not normally supplied. In the opinion of the author the replacement of these by galvanised thimbles, although it might alter slightly the frictional force between the rope and the thimble, would not have any major effect on the performance of the terminations up to the slip initiation point.

It is interesting to note that if the graphs in Fig.5 are extrapolated back towards zero they all intersect the X axis at torques of 5 - 7 lbf.ft (6 - 9 Nm). This represents the initial torque lost in friction which does not contribute to the strength of the termination. Similarly the graphs for three and four ungalvanised grips (Fig.6) also pass through the axis at about 5 lbf.ft (6 Nm). The graph for five ungalvanised grips has a less steep gradient but examination of the detailed results (Fig.A1.7) shows that at 40 lbf.ft torque (54 Nm) wires began to break before the termination slipped. If this had not happened higher slip loads would have been achieved. The data at the top end of the graph is not very reliable therefore and as a consequence an alternative graph has been drawn (with a dashed line at a steeper gradient) to take this fact in account and to allow the line to intersect the X axis at 5 lbf.ft (6 Nm) torque. Whether this dashed line is a truer performance indicator than the original full line for five ungalvanised grips could only be established by further tests over a slightly different torque range.

In the preliminary tests to establish the test procedure it was noted that, when using galvanised grips, greasing the U bolt threads before use resulted in slightly higher termination efficiencies. Insufficient tests were carried out for a proper quantitative assessment to be made but it appeared that the greased threads gave termination efficiencies about 5% to 10% higher than ungreased threads. These results have not been included on the graphs to avoid confusion for the tests conditions were slightly different to those of the main programme.

It was also observed that with almost every grip the two legs of the U bolt were not parallel and this misalignment caused the corners of the nuts to dig into the surface of the bridge piece (Fig.4), especially when galvanised. As mentioned earlier the average error in the alignment of the U bolt legs was about 5 deg. In some preliminary tests washers were placed under the nuts but on tightening the grips the misalignment of the U bolt legs simply caused the edges of the washers to be forced into the zinc coating and there appeared to be no significant improvement in termination efficiency. The use of washers was not included in the main programme. Experience showed that after the first tightening of the grips up to about 40% of the applied torque could be lost in the first few hours, even when the rope was not loaded. A similar fall-off in torque was noted after applying a load to the rope. Both these drops were caused by the bedding down of the rope strands into the fibre main cores. The torques remaining on the grips after each test were recorded; there was a large scatter in the torque lost on individual nuts in each termination but generally the final mean torque values were about 60% of the pre-test torque value regardless of whether a high or low torque had been used in a particular test.

PART 1 - SUMMARY

None of the BS 462 grips purchased new in the period 1984 to 1986 had been manufactured to either the BS 462:1969 or 1983 specifications. The dimensions of most of the grips corresponded with those given in the obsolete BS 462:1958 but a few of the U bolts were well outside the dimensional tolerance limits given in all three editions of the Standard.

The original Appendix A to BS 462: 1983 recommended a minimum of three grips on a 16 mm diameter rope to give a termination efficiency of 80%. BS 462:1958 and 1969 indicated the same numbers of grips should give efficiencies of 85% to 90% based on the actual breaking load of the rope. The results from these tests show clearly that with only three galvanised grips (Fig.5) at torque levels that might be used in service the efficiency is only of the order of 15% to 20%.

To achieve efficiencies of 80% more than three galvanised grips are needed. The user has the option of either using more than six grips at low torques or at least five grips at higher torques, but in the latter case special fitting equipment to hold the rope and the grips, and to apply the torque whilst it is being put on, would probably be required. In addition the higher torques could damage the rope.

When ungalvanised grips and thimbles are used the termination efficiencies are roughly double those obtained with galvanised grips and thimbles under the same conditions. The tests indicated that five or more ungalvanised grips per termination would be required to reach the 80% efficiency level at practical torque values. It must be re-emphasised however that galvanised grips should always be used on a galvanised rope. It is not generally permissible to increase termination efficiency by simply changing from galvanised to ungalvanised BS 462 grips, adding extra grips is a more realistic solution.

There is a serious loss of torque on grips with time, especially on fibre cored ropes. With a new rope up to 40% of the initial torque applied to the nuts can be lost over a 12 hour period due to the bedding-down of the strands under the individual grips even when the rope remains unloaded.

Although the majority of grips are used as supplied it was shown that applying extra grease to the threads on the U bolt legs before use resulted in slightly higher termination efficiencies.

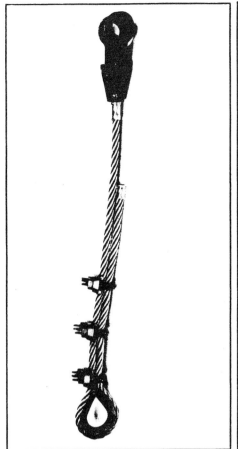

8411-045/7

Fig.1 - Test sample

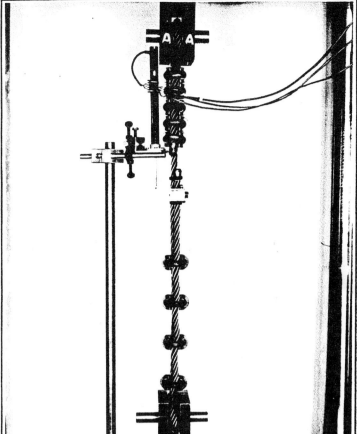

8502-050/10

Fig.2 - Test termination fastened to lower fixed crosshead of testing machine

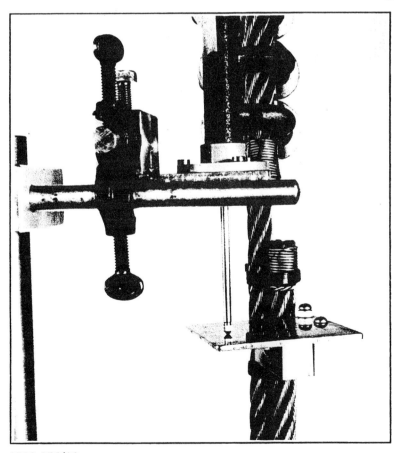

Figs.2 & 3 - These photographs were taken during earlier tests and show wire rope grips used to hold the live end of the rope instead of a white metal capping

8502-050/12

Fig.3 - Slip detection transducer and reference plate on tail end of rope

Fig.4 Effect of misalignment of U bolt legs

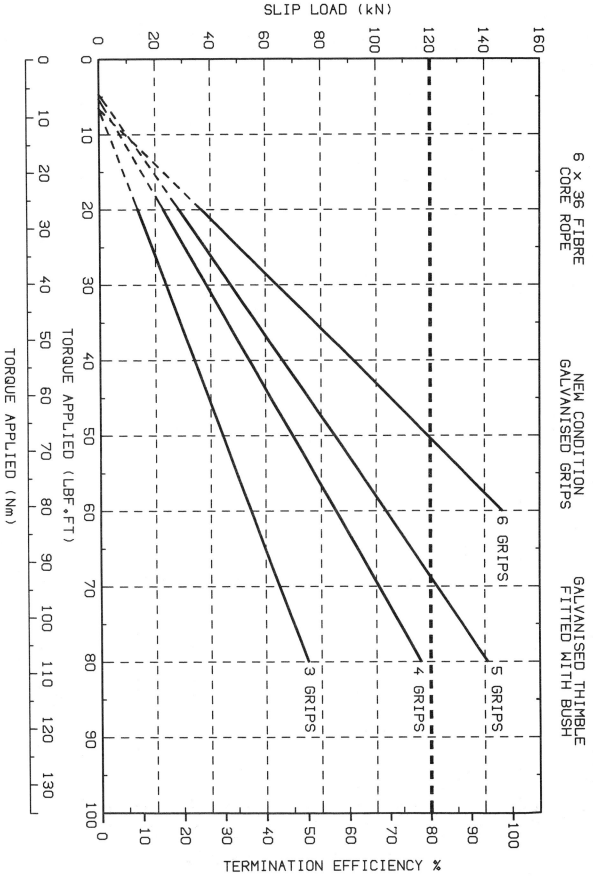

BS462 16mm WIRE ROPE GRIPS

ROPE MINIMUM BREAKING LOAD (BS302 Part 2:1987) = 150kN

6 × 36 FIBRE
CORE ROPE

NEW CONDITION
GALVANISED GRIPS

GALVANISED THIMBLE
FITTED WITH BUSH

Fig.5 Slip Load v. Initial Torque for 16mm galvanised grips

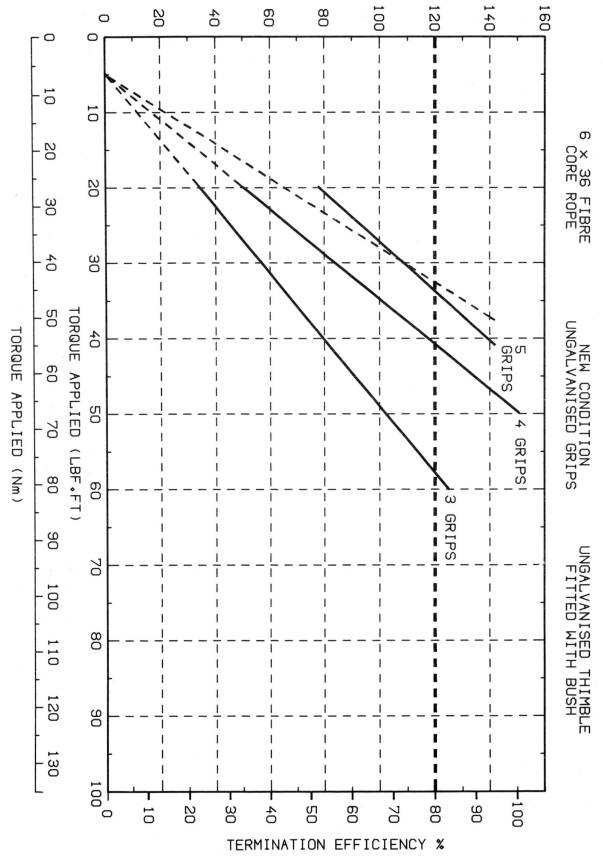

Fig.6 Slip Load v. Initial Torque for 16mm ungalvanised grips

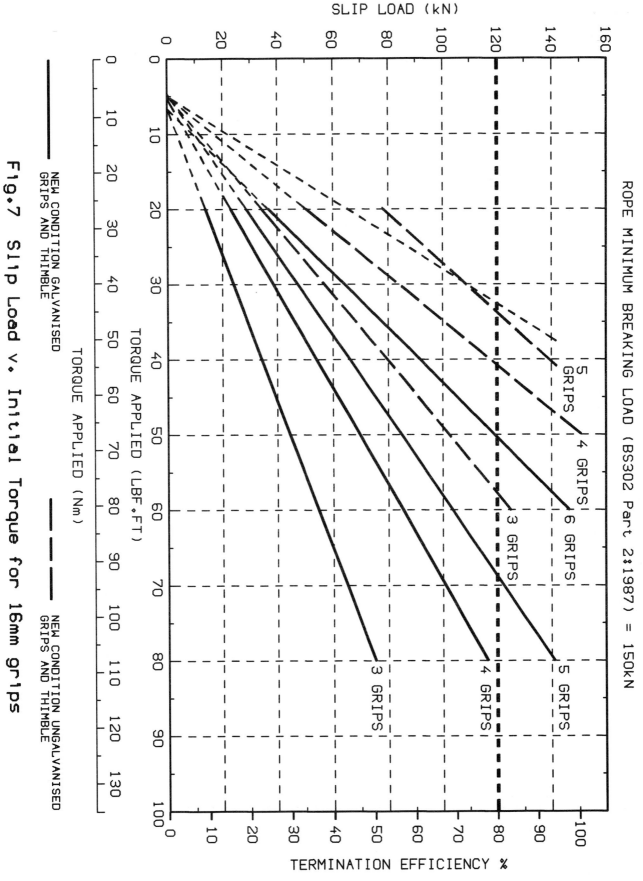

Fig.7 Slip Load v. Initial Torque for 16mm grips

APPENDIX 1

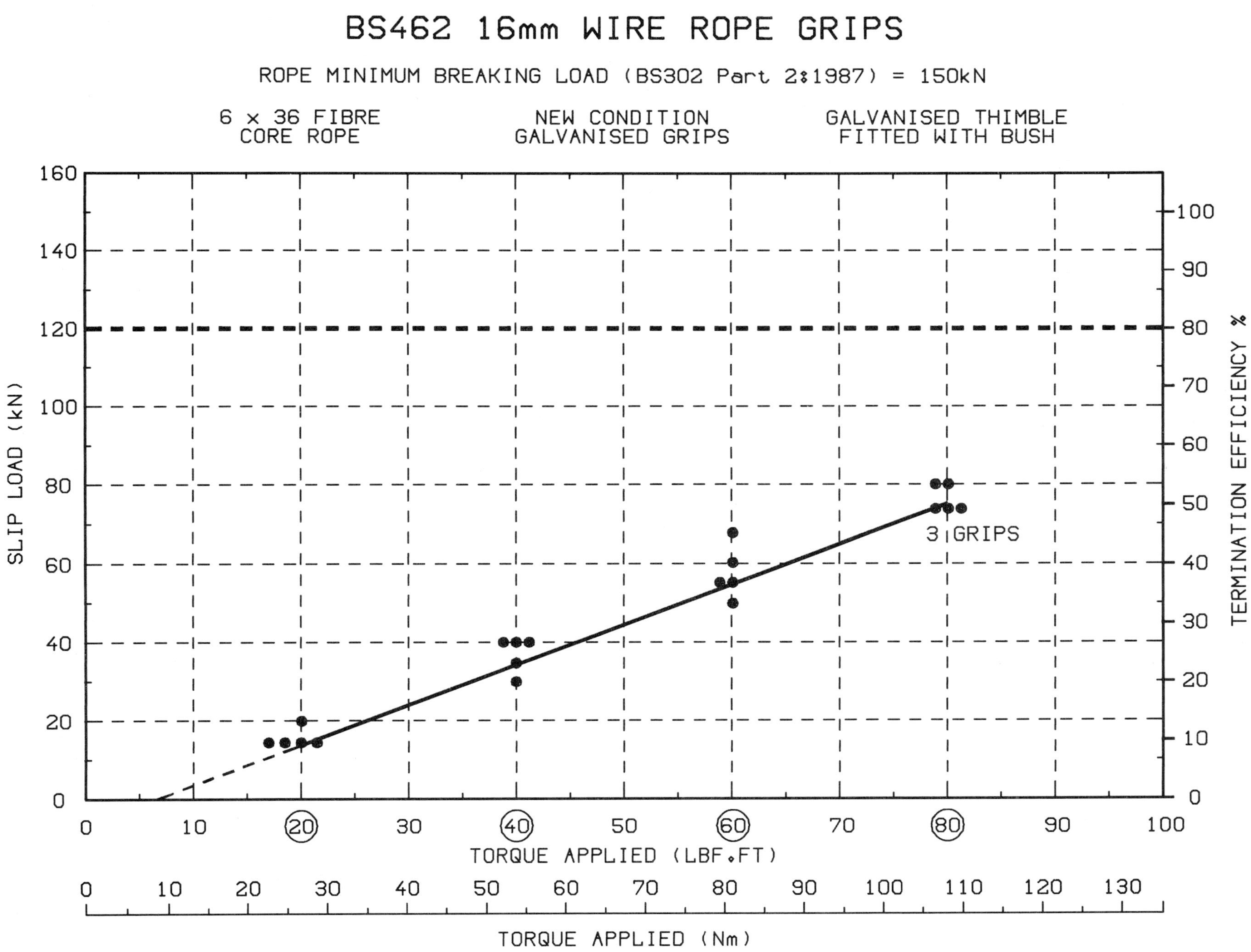
BS462 16mm WIRE ROPE GRIPS
ROPE MINIMUM BREAKING LOAD (BS302 Part 2:1987) = 150kN
6 x 36 FIBRE CORE ROPE
NEW CONDITION GALVANISED GRIPS
GALVANISED THIMBLE FITTED WITH BUSH
SLIP LOAD (kN)
0
20
40
60
80
100
120
140
160
TERMINATION EFFICIENCY %
0
10
20
30
40
50
60
70
80
90
100
3 GRIPS
TORQUE APPLIED (LBF.FT)
0
10
20
30
40
50
60
70
80
90
100
TORQUE APPLIED (Nm)
0
10
20
30
40
50
60
70
80
90
100
110
120
130

Fig.A1.1

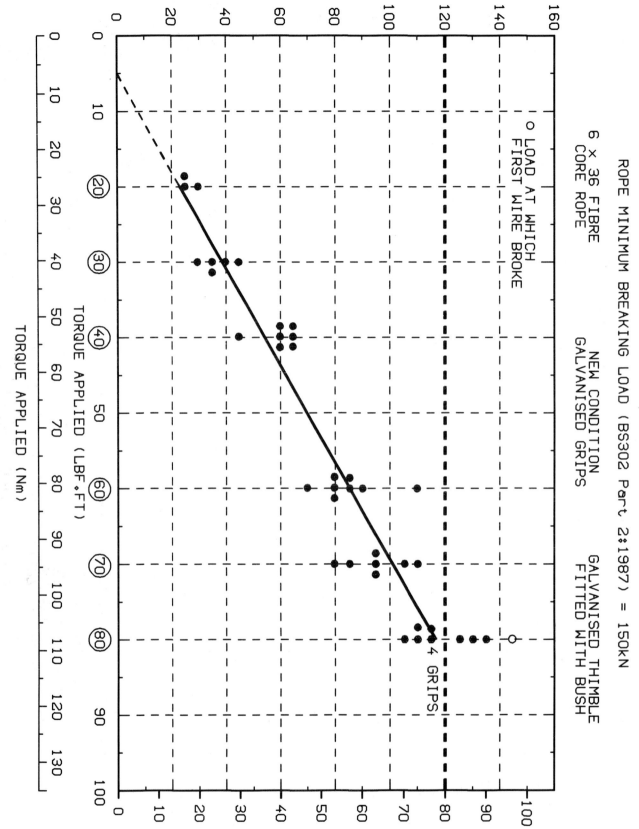

BS462 16mm WIRE ROPE GRIPS

Fig.A1.2

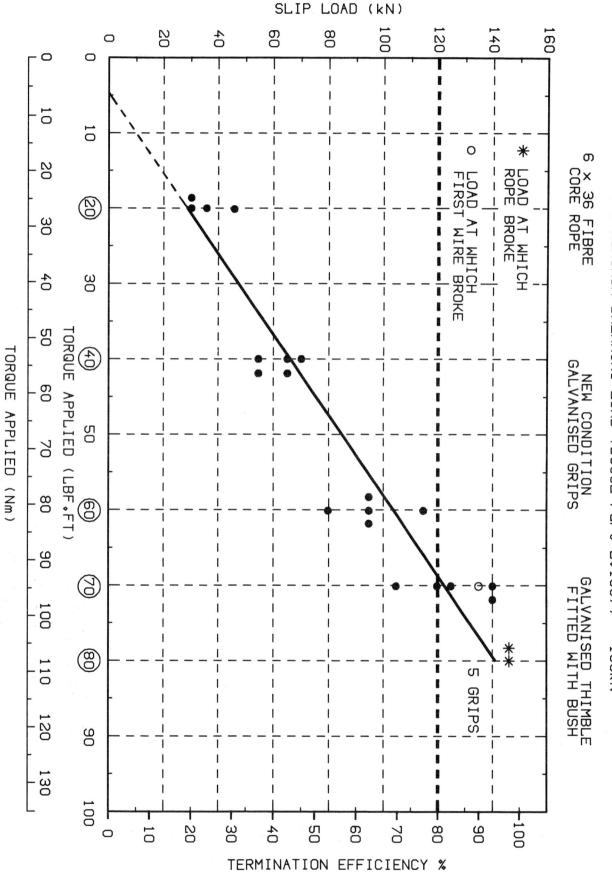

Fig. A1.3

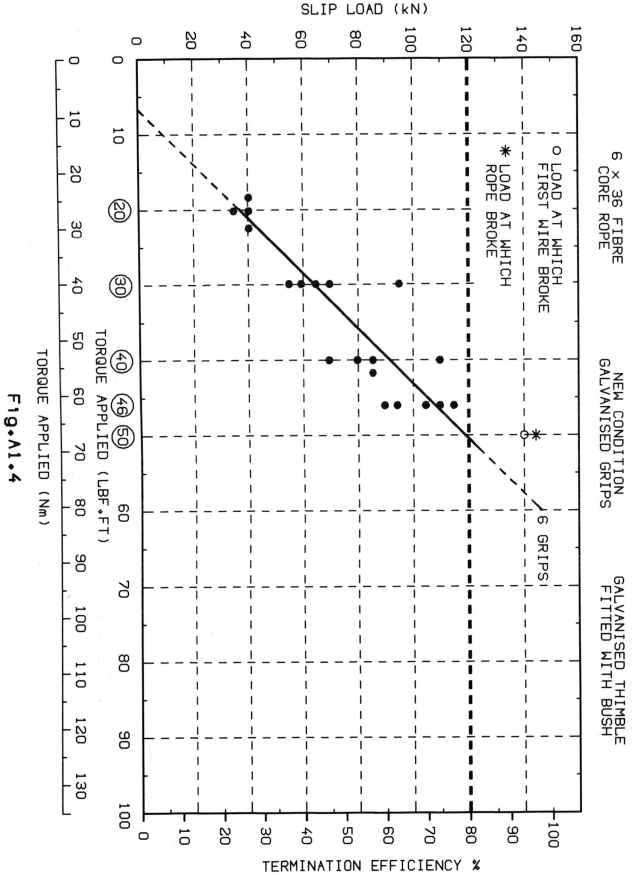

BS462 16mm WIRE ROPE GRIPS

ROPE MINIMUM BREAKING LOAD (BS302 Part 2:1987) = 150kN

6 × 36 FIBRE CORE ROPE

NEW CONDITION GALVANISED GRIPS

GALVANISED THIMBLE FITTED WITH BUSH

SLIP LOAD (kN)

○ LOAD AT WHICH FIRST WIRE BROKE

∗ LOAD AT WHICH ROPE BROKE

6 GRIPS

TORQUE APPLIED (LBF.FT)

TORQUE APPLIED (Nm)

TERMINATION EFFICIENCY %

Fig.A1.4

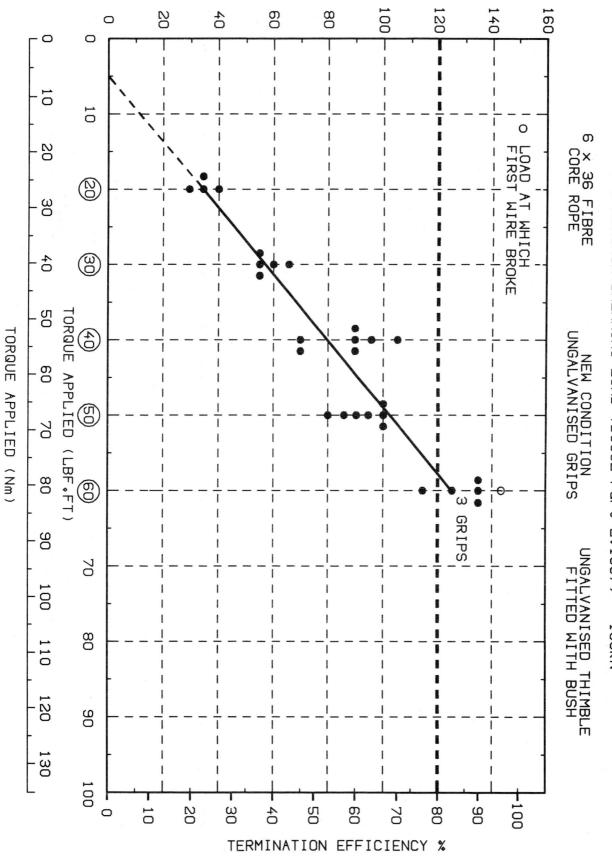

Fig.A1.5

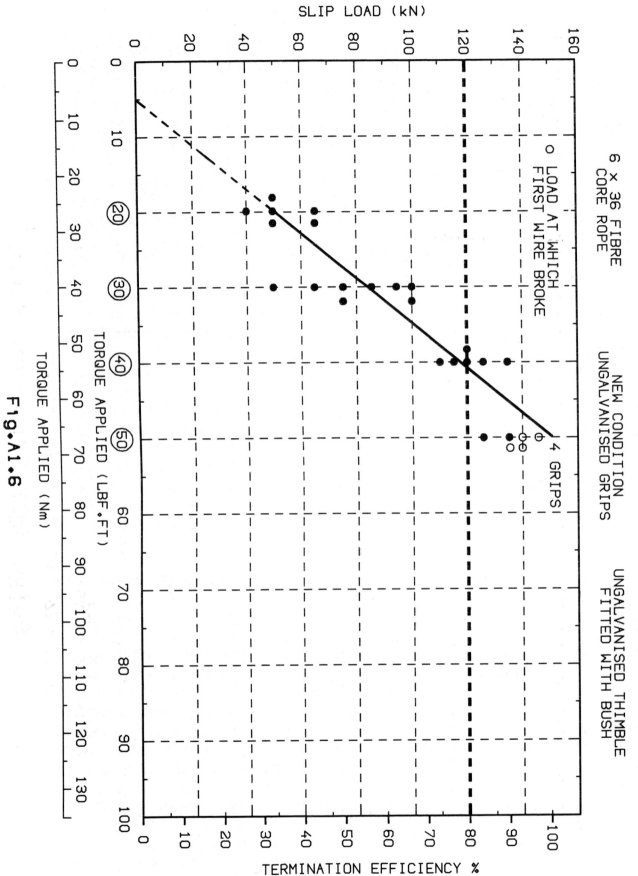

Fig.A1.6

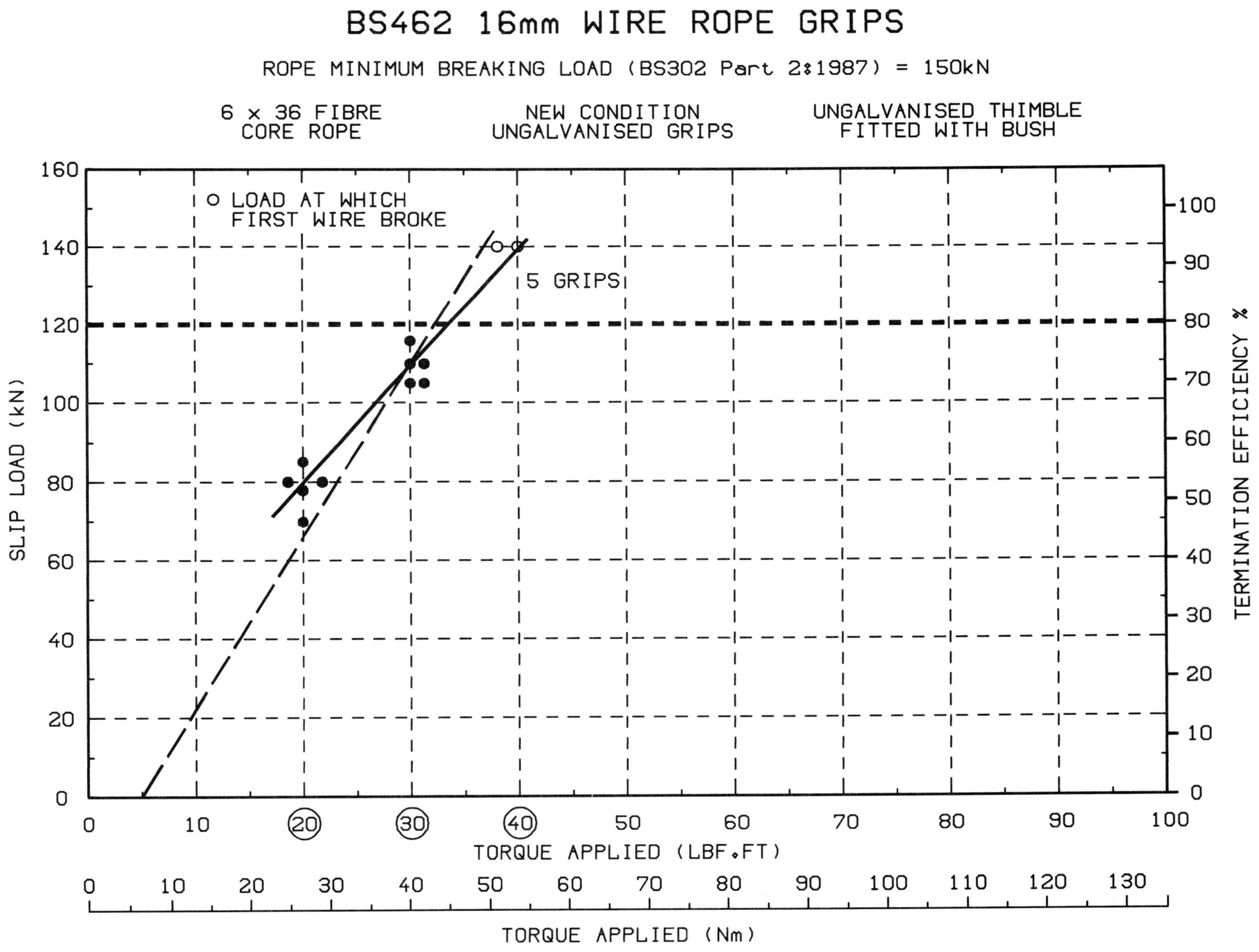

BS462 16mm WIRE ROPE GRIPS

ROPE MINIMUM BREAKING LOAD (BS302 Part 2:1987) = 150kN

6 x 36 FIBRE
CORE ROPE

NEW CONDITION
UNGALVANISED GRIPS

UNGALVANISED THIMBLE
FITTED WITH BUSH

SLIP LOAD (kN)

TORQUE APPLIED

TORQUE APPLIED (LBF.FT)

TORQUE APPLIED (Nm)

TERMINATION EFFICIENCY %

○ LOAD AT WHICH
FIRST WIRE BROKE

5 GRIPS

Fig.A1.7

PART 2

The first part of this paper covered details of the method used to test terminations made using wire rope grips, general observations about the quality of BS 462 grips, and features which affect their performance in service. Part 1 then discussed the results from Phase 1 of the programme where the effects of using different numbers of grips in each termination and the torques applied to them were investigated. Part 2 discusses some of the effects of time on the torque on the grips and highlights the problem of measuring torque values without re-torquing the grips at the same time. The results of tests on four different rope constructions of 16 mm diameter rope, and five different sizes of rope of one construction are also summarised. This part concludes with a brief discussion of the problems encounted whilst trying to determine the effects of wear on BS 462 grips.

It should be noted that as a result of the research reported in this paper BS 462 was eventually withdrawn in 1991. Large numbers of grips purporting to have been made to BS 462 remain in service however and will continue to be used for many years.

RESULTS AND DISCUSSION OF TESTS (Continued from Part 1)

PHASE 2 - The effects of time, load cycling, and re-torquing on the termination efficiency

The aim of this phase of the programme was to investigate the loss of torque with time using both loaded and unloaded terminations, the effects of load cycling, and the effects of re-torquing.

In this phase all of the 65 tests were carried out on terminations made using three new galvanised BS 462 grips and a new galvanised BS 464 thimble fitted with a bush to reduce its distortion. All the tests were made using test lengths from the same ungalvanised 16 mm 6x36(14/7and7/7/1)FC stranded rope as used for phase 1.

It was noted in Part 1 that the BS 462 grips purchased in the period 1984 -1986 for this programme did not meet the dimensional requirements of either BS 462:1983 or the earlier BS 462:1969. They had been manufactured to the dimensions given in BS 462:1958 which became obsolete in 1971.

The reduction in torque with time on unloaded specimens

The first tests in this phase were to study the reduction in torque with time with unloaded specimens. Seven tests were made in which the torque was measured at approximately daily or weekly intervals until an equilibrium situation was reached. All the unloaded test specimens were identical, they were stored together, there was no significant change in the ambient temperature over the test period, and the same torque meter was used for all the checks which were carried out by the same person.

The results of these tests are shown in Fig.8. Each plotted point on the graph represents the mean value of the torques on the six nuts in each three grip termination at a particular time. Lines have been drawn on Fig.8 between points in each test, but it must be emphasised that these lines do not follow actual torque v. time paths. For example the initial loss of torque from a given starting value would be the same over the first few hours regardless of whether the test specimens were to be checked at daily or weekly intervals. The initial fall in torque would probably be rapid but then the torque would semi-stabilise until the grips were disturbed by the action of taking another reading. After taking each reading, which involves a slight re-torquing of each grip (see below), there would probably follow a further period of fairly rapid re-adjustment or fall in torque before it stabilised again. Thus it could be expected that the actual torque values measured were related both to the number of torque measurements taken and to the time interval between such measurements.

The daily measurement tests showed a loss of torque from all three starting values for the first three days, followed by what appeared to be a slight recovery rise and then a general levelling off. A similar pattern was produced from the weekly measurement tests - in these cases an initial loss occurred over the first two weeks (two cases), and over the first three weeks in the third case, after which the torque values seemed to stabilise or even to rise slightly. The explanation for the rise in torque after the initial fall-off period is that when using a conventional torque meter it is necessary to apply an increasing torque to each nut until the nut just begins to turn, and then to maintain this torque long enough for the meter reading to be taken. In practice the amount of rotation of the nut which occurs whilst this is being done is about 60 deg (i.e. one flat on the nut). This turning of each nut effectively re-torques it slightly, so that the greater the number of readings taken the more each nut is re-torqued. A level curve in Fig.8 indicates that the fall-off or loss of torque between readings is balanced by the re-torquing effect of taking those readings. Only a slightly rising line would indicate that no further loss in torque had occurred between measurements.

The initial loss in the mean torque before the re-torquing effect became obvious in the 80, 50, and 30 lbf.ft (108, 68, and 41 Nm) cases was 29%, 42% and 50% respectively for the daily measurements and 29%, 27% and 41% respectively for the weekly measurements. These results are not statistically significant because of the few tests carried out but they seem to confirm that the actual values obtained are more closely related to the number of previous torque measurements taken rather than the interval between measurements. The results do indicate that the loss in torque is greater where lower initial torques are applied. This suggests that higher torques, although possibly causing some initial crushing damage, tend to stabilise the rope construction earlier, reducing the possibility of longer term creep effects.

The effects of holding a load for short periods

Twenty seven tests were carried out to study the effects of holding a load equal to the Safe Working Load (SWL) on the rope, assuming a Factor of Safety of 5 as recommended in BS 6570:1986, for different relatively short periods of time. In each three grip termination the six nuts were torqued up to the same value. Tests were carried out with the terminations torqued up to 80, 50, and 30 lbf.ft (108, 68, and 41 Nm) whilst the terminations were subjected to a small holding load of 3 kN. A load of 30 kN (equivalent to the SWL) was then applied to each specimen and held in different tests for periods of 5 min, 1 hour, and 5 hours respectively. At the end of the test period the residual torque on the nuts was measured before the 30 kN load was removed. These tests represent the worst situation which could arise is service i.e. where the grips are torqued up under no load, or very low load conditions, and then the maximum service load is hung on the rope and left without re-torquing the grips.

In each of the 27 tests there were appreciable variations between the residual torques on the six individual nuts of each termination after the tests. The six values from each test were therefore averaged, and the mean value obtained compared with the mean value from the two repeat tests at the same data point. The mean values from the six nuts in individual terminations lay between 96% (Test torque 50 lbf.ft, load held for 5 min) and 62% (Test torque 30 lbf.ft, load held for 1 hour) of the original torques applied in the respective cases. The average of the three mean values from each data point are shown in the following table.

31

Applied torque at zero load lbf.ft (Nm)	Load held kN	Residual torque as a % of the original torque (measured at 30 kN load) after periods under load of		
		5 min	1 hr	5 hr
30 (41)	30	84.8	75.9	82.6
50 (68)	30	96.1	83.3	89.4
80 (108)	30	81.8	76.8	83.0

These results were inconclusive because of the wide scatter and the small number of tests carried out at each data point. The results indicated that the mean residual torques after one hour were less than after five minutes, but as two of the mean values after five hours lay between the 5 min and 1 hour figures, and the third was higher than the corresponding 5 min value, the results showed no clear trends.

By comparison terminations left unloaded as in the previous part of the programme showed mean residual torques after one day in the range 50% to 71% of their original values.

It is also interesting to note that in the tests with torques of 30 lbf.ft (41 Nm) slip was detected on most occasions before the applied load had reached 30 kN, or whilst this load was being held. Loading the termination very slowly from 25 kN seemed to help the grips to get a stronger hold.

After the completion of the first part of these tests the grips were re-torqued to their initial test values, whilst under a small load of 3 kN, and the slip initiation loads of the termination measured as in Phase 1 of this programme. The results from the slip load tests are given in Fig.9. A linear regression method was used to plot the results from the terminations used for the previous 5 min, 1 hour, and 5 hour held load tests, and from all 27 points taken together. There was a fairly wide scatter in the results and no really conclusive evidence that the earlier different periods of holding a 30 kN load had made any significant difference. When the line calculated from all 27 points was plotted on the same graph as the results from phase 1 (Fig.10) then the later tests showed a small increase in slip load, or termination efficiency, throughout the range of torques used. This increase could have been due to the bedding in effect of holding a 30 kN load before carrying out the slip load tests but it is more likely that this increase was due to the fact that the grips had been re-torqued between the two parts of each test. It was noted that in the case of those tests carried out using a torque of 30 lbf.ft (41 Nm), slip had occurred in most cases at loads below 30 kN in the first part of these tests, whereas in the second part, after re-torquing, the slip loads had risen to 30 kN or above.

The effects of holding a load for long periods

In this part of the programme the effects of holding a constant static load for very much longer periods was investigated with particular emphasis on the rate of slip with time. Loading was achieved by hanging a concrete block of approximately 3 ton mass from the termination, this produced a load in the rope of about 30 kN (i.e. the

SWL for the rope when using a Factor of Safety of 5). For these tests the original loading rig and slip measuring instrumentation could not be used so a separate loading rig was built and a dial gauge was substituted for the computer controlled instrumentation to measure the slip. In practice this gauge was only capable of measuring displacements of 0.01 mm so it was not capable of detecting the small microstrain slip movement measured in the other phases of this programme.

In the first two tests the three grips forming the termination were torqued up to 30 lbf.ft (41 Nm) before the load was hung on the rope. The torques were re-checked as soon as the load was applied. Slip movements on the tail side of the terminations were read from the dial gauge. The readings were initially taken at hourly intervals but later the frequency was reduced to daily; the results are shown in Fig.11. In both cases the detected slip was fairly rapid for the first hour but then decreased sharply. At the end of the first 24 hours the terminations had slipped about 1 mm and 2 mm respectively. The rate of slip then decreased progressively with time, but nevertheless continued, until after 40 days movement had slowed down to about 0.005 mm per day. At this stage the rope in the first termination had slipped a total of 3.15 mm and the rope in the second termination 2.16 mm.

At the completion of these tests the residual torque on each nut was measured. The average torque on the six nuts in each termination was 18.8 and 18.5 lbf.ft (25.6 and 25.2 Nm) respectively (i.e. 62.6% and 61.7% of the original torque). This loss of torque was much less than expected from the phase 1 results where 40% drops were measured in a few hours. In these tests it appears that the important features were the re-torquing of the grips after the load had been hung from the rope and the static nature of the loading.

Three tests were made with the nuts torqued up to 25 lbf.ft (34 Nm) under no load conditions, in all three tests there was immediate slip when the load was hung on the rope. This initial slip movement was 12.7 mm, 6.1 mm, and 1.9 mm respectively (Fig.12).

In the first of these tests the slip reached 15.7 mm within 30 min but it then slowed down, reaching 16.8 mm after 7 hours. Slip continued thereafter at approximately 0.05 mm per day reaching 17.9 mm on the 15th day. At the cessation of this test the residual torques on the nuts varied between 4 lbf.ft (5 Nm) and 15 lbf.ft (20 Nm), average 11 lbf.ft (15 Nm), i.e an average of 44% of the original torque applied.

In the second of these tests the pattern of slip was very similar, the initial 6.1 mm reaching 9.7 mm after 6.5 hours and 11.3 mm after 16 days. The rate of slip was approximately 0.1 mm per day for much of the test period but slowed to about 0.02 mm per day after the tenth day. At the cessation of the test the residual torque varied from 8 lbf.ft (11 Nm) to 18 lbf.ft (24 Nm), average 13 lbf.ft (18 Nm) i.e. approx 50% of the original value.

In the third of these tests the initial rapid slip had reached 4.4 mm within 30 min so the torque on each nut was checked. It was found that two of the nuts had lost

5 lbf.ft (7 Nm) but the others remained at 25 lbf.ft (34 Nm) or above, the actual torques on these four nuts were not determined because to do so would have effectively added a small extra torque to each nut. The test was continued and after 4 hours the slip had reached 6.4 mm. The rate of slip then decreased appreciably to about 0.2 mm per day, and later to 0.05 mm per day, reaching 8.6 mm after 23 days. At the cessation of this test the thimble had rotated about 20 deg and the residual torque on the nuts varied from 9 lbf.ft (12 Nm) to 24 lbf.ft (33 Nm), average 16 lbf.ft (22 Nm) i.e about 64% of the original value.

These results indicate the large change in the initial slip rates which can occur for relatively small changes in the torquing values i.e from 30 lbf.ft (41 Nm) (see Fig.11) to 25 lbf.ft (34 Nm) (see Fig.12), especially when the grips are not re-torqued after the application of the load (as in Fig.12).

Three tests were made with the grips torqued up to 20 lbf.ft (27 Nm). In the first of these the grips were torqued-up with no load on the rope, but as soon as the weight was hung from it the rope began to slip through the termination. The results are shown in Fig.13. The initial slip was rapid and easily visible, totalling 9.35 mm in the first hour which caused the thimble points to rotate in the eye of the termination. The rate of slip then decreased dramatically reaching 11.53 mm after five hours and 13.16 mm after 9 days when the test was stopped. At the end of 9 days slip was continuing at a very slow but steady rate of approx 0.08 mm per day. At this point the thimble had rotated about 30 deg within the eye. It appeared that the initial rapid slip had continued until the points of the thimble began to bite into the rope - this is a feature which had been noted previously in another programme of work whilst testing terminations made with similar grips and thimbles under rapid slip conditions. At the end of 9 days the residual torque on individual nuts in the termination used in this first test varied from 3 lbf.ft (4 Nm) to 18 lbf.ft (24 Nm), which gave an average remaining torque of 10 lbf.ft (14 Nm), i.e. 50% of the original.

The two following tests at the same torque value of 20 lbf.ft (27 Nm) also showed rapid slip as soon as the load was hung from the termination but in these tests the grips were immediately re-torqued. This action reduced the rate of slip dramatically so that after the re-torquing the slip after one hour measured 0.58 mm and approx 1.5 mm respectively. At the conclusion of these tests slip had totalled 1.75 mm after 20 days and 4.14 mm after 28 days respectively, the final rates of slip being about 0.03 and 0.02 mm per day. The results are shown in Fig.13. The remaining torque averaged 14.7 lbf.ft (20 Nm), i.e. 73.3% of the original torque, in the first of these tests; after the second it was not recorded. The second of these two tests was chronologically the last test in this part of the programme so the load was left hanging on the rope for a further 18 months, slip was continuous throughout this period but at a very slow rate. The actual rate varied slightly over the 18 months, possibly because the test rig although under cover was exposed to climatic temperature changes, it averaged about 0.001 mm per day over the 18 month period. These last two tests illustrate the importance of re-torquing the grips as soon as the full load has been applied.

The effects of re-torquing

The aim of this part of the programme was to study the loss of torque on the nuts after periodic re-torquing. This work was abandoned because as explained earlier each measurement of torque involved turning the nut about 60 deg which in effect also slightly re-torqued it.

With hindsight it would have been possible, even if tedious, to mark the position of each nut on each grip leg after the initial torque had been applied and then after each torque measurement had been taken to twist the nut back to its original position on that leg. This process would have introduced some additional experimental errors but it could have partly overcome the re-torquing problem when measuring torque values during a test.

The effects of cyclic loading

In this phase of the work twenty one tests were carried out to study the effects of load cycling on the torque on the nuts and on the eventual slip load. In these tests the initial torque was put on whilst there was only a low load on the rope, the load was then raised to the Safe Working Load for the rope (i.e. 30 kN in this case assuming a Factor of Safety of 5) and held there for five minutes. At this point the torque remaining on each nut was measured. The load was removed and then re-applied, this process being repeated 30 times without any hold period at 30 kN. The torque remaining on each nut whilst the termination was under load was checked (a) every fifth cycle (one test only), and (b) after 30 cycles. After the thirtieth cycle the load was raised until slip was detected, the load was then removed and the residual torque measured.

Although there were wide variations in the torque values measured on individual nuts, in general the average values for the six nuts on the three grips in each termination remained fairly constant. When the mean values for the six nuts on each termination were also averaged for the different load cycles all the values lay between 85.3% and 89.8% of the initial torque values - there being very little difference between the grips torqued to 30, 50, 65, or 80 lbf.ft (41, 68, 88, and 108 Nm). At the end of the test after slip had been produced the averaged no load torque lay between 66.6% and 71.9% of the original no load value for all four initial torques. It should not be forgotten that in these tests each measurement of torque would have had a small re-torquing effect on the nuts, so the true loss of torque during each test would have been greater than that measured.

The slip initiation points determined after the 30 load cycles had been applied are shown in Fig.14, these only differ significantly from the results obtained in phase 1 at the low torque end of the scale suggesting that the 30 load cycles simply helped to bed-in the rope more at low torques. At the higher torques most of the bedding-in probably occurred during torquing up, or in the first cycle, so the additional cycles had very little effect on the final slip point.

PHASE 3 - The Effects of Rope Construction

The aim of this part of the programme was to investigate the effects of different rope constructions on the slip load, or efficiency, of the termination.

All the tests in this part of the programme were carried out on 16mm diameter rope. The tests were made with new galvanised BS 462 grips and new galvanised thimbles. The grips were used as supplied, i.e. the U bolt and nut threads were not greased. Washers were not used under the nuts.

Tests were carried out on terminations made using three, four or five grips. All the grips in any termination were torqued up to the same value whilst only a small load of about 3 kN was on the rope. Tests were then carried out as in phase 1 so that graphs of torque v. slip initiation load could be plotted.

Four rope constructions were tested, these were:

             (1) 6x36 FC ungalvanised (results taken from Phase 1)
             (2) 6x36 IWRC galvanised
             (3) 17x7 Multistrand ungalvanised
             (4) 6x19 FC ungalvanised

The particular multistrand rope used in these tests was of Lang's lay construction. This is not a construction which is really suitable for use with wire rope grip terminations because the strands tend to try to unlay themselves if allowed to twist. The action of tightening up the grips on such a rope would cause some unlaying of the strands under each grip which would reduce the effective diameter of the rope and cause earlier slip than with a rope of ordinary lay. The use of this Lang's lay rope in these tests therefore was an attempt to simulate the worst possible condition which might arise in service.

A total of 131 tests were made in this phase. The results for three grips per termination are shown in Fig.15, for four grips per termination in Fig.16, and for five grips per termination in Fig.17.

The results from the tests using three grips per termination indicate a close similarity between the three constructions with fibre main cores. The rope with the independent wire rope core (IWRC) gave a higher efficiency at all points but this was particularly noticeable at the higher torque values. It should be noted however that the IWRC rope still showed less than 30% efficiency at a torque value of 30 lbf.ft (41 Nm) - about the practical service torque limit when using 16 mm grips in many applications.

It should be noted also that with three grips on the Lang's lay multistrand rope the efficiency was only of the order of 13% at a torque of 30 lbf.ft (41 Nm). With three grips on the other two fibre cored ropes efficiencies were also below 20% at this torque. When the reduction in the torque with time, or after the application of a load, is taken into consideration efficiencies as low as this must be a cause of concern.

36

Only two constructions were tested with four grips: the 6x36 FC rope and the 6x36 IWRC rope. The results are summarised in Fig.16. The IWRC rope gave the higher results at all points, but at 30 lbf.ft (41 Nm) torque the efficiency was still only about 43%. At the same torque with the FC rope the efficiency was about 27%.

The results obtained when using five grips are summarised in Fig.17.

The relative differences in the results when using five grips are very similar to those obtained with three grips. The three fibre cored ropes giving similar efficiencies whilst the IWRC rope gave appreciably higher values. At the practical torque of 30 lbf.ft (41 Nm) the efficiency of the termination on the IWRC rope, about 58%, was approximately double that of the fibre cored ropes.

The main conclusion which can be drawn from these tests on ropes of different construction is that it is only the type of main rope core which makes any really significant difference to the efficiency of the terminations. It should also be noted that the 80% efficiency level was achieved with five galvanised BS 462 grips on the IWRC rope at a torque value of about 40 lbf.ft (54 Nm) only a little above the practical service torque of 30 lbf.ft (41 Nm) discussed in Part 1 of this paper, so with six galvanised BS 462 grips on a steel cored rope an 80% efficiency should be achievable in practice. Extrapolation from the results obtained in Phase 1 with galvanised BS 462 grips on the 6x36 FC rope suggests that on ropes with fibre main cores the 80% termination efficiency level would only be achieved at a practical torque of about 30 lbf.ft (41 Nm) by using either seven or eight grips in each termination.

PHASE 4 - Size Effects

The aim of this part of the programme was to investigate the effect of rope size on the efficiency of the terminations.

In this phase tests were carried out on four different sizes of rope of the same 6x36(14/7and7/7/1)FC ungalvanised construction. The sizes chosen for these tests were 9, 13, 16, and 19 mm diameter. Unfortunately ropes larger than 19 mm diameter could not be tested in the available test machine because the test specimens became too long to fit into the space between the crossheads. In each test the grips used were of the same nominal size as the rope to which they were fitted.

The four sizes of rope were tested using three grip terminations. Three sizes were also tested with five grips terminations.

A few additional tests were made using 14 mm diameter rope because grips to BS 462 are not made specifically for this size. The nearest grip size which can be fitted is 16 mm but using these grips on a 14 mm dia rope allows the ropes to distort to a slightly oval shape within the U bolt of the grip. The extra tests were made to see whether this difference in size between the rope and the grips had any significant effect on the termination efficiency.

A total of 101 tests were carried out in this phase. The results from the three grip tests are summarised in Fig.18, and those using five grips per termination in Fig.19.

The results for three grips per termination (Fig.18) show very marked decreases in efficiency with increases in rope diameter up to 16 mm. The values for 19 mm rope are very similar to those for a 16 mm rope when the restricted number of tests and normal experimental variations and errors are taken into consideration. It may also be relevant that the rod from which the U bolts had been made for the 19 mm grips was the same diameter as that used for the 16 mm grips as given in BS 462:1958, but this is about 30% undersize for 19 mm grips according to BS 462, Part 2:1969 and BS 462:1983.

In interpreting Fig.18 it must not be forgotten that the practical torques which would be applied to the nuts in service also vary with the grip size. For example with the 9 mm rope and 3 grips although the tests indicated 100% efficiency at 20 lbf.ft (27 Nm) the distortion in the rope under the hoop of the U bolt at this value is considerable and could give rise to fatigue problems in service. For this size of rope and grip a torque in the range 10 - 15 lbf.ft (14 - 20 Nm), or even lower, would probably be more acceptable. Similarly with the 13 mm rope and 3 grips although efficiencies of about 77% were indicated from the tests at a torque of 40 lbf.ft (54 Nm) the use of more realistic torques in the range 20 - 25 lbf.ft (27 - 33 Nm) would bring the efficiencies below 40%. In the laboratory tests the torque could be applied relatively easily on the single pre-tensioned specimens, on the other hand under many service conditions applying the same torque could be much more difficult or even impractical in some cases.

When the family of lines for the different grip sizes is studied as a whole (Fig.18) it can be seen that all but the 9 mm lines can be extrapolated back so that they intersect the zero efficiency line at torque values of from about 4 lbf.ft (5 Nm) to about 7 lbf.ft (10 Nm); these values representing the torque absorbed by friction under no load conditions. Under similar conditions the 9 mm line would be expected to intersect the zero efficiency line in the same region. A similar observation was made after the phase 1 tests using five ungalvanised grips (Fig.5) where high efficiencies at low torques were also measured.

Examination of the seventeen individual test results for the 9 mm grips showed a bigger scatter in the results at low torques than with the larger sizes of grip, whilst at the highest torque used, 20 lbf.ft (27 Nm), in five out of six tests the rope broke at the grips before the slip initiation point was reached. The scatter at the low torque end could have been due in part to limitations of the load and torque measuring equipment, both items being used at the lower extremities of their operating ranges. As with the phase 1 results (Fig.5) at the top end of the graph the breakages of the ropes distort the picture and the same efficiencies might have been achieved without breakage using slightly lower torques. After making allowances for these factors it is the opinion of the author that the alternative dashed line shown on Fig.18 for the 9 mm grips could perhaps be a little nearer to the true performance characteristic or that a slightly curved characteristic rather than a straight line one might apply in this region. Further tests would be needed to investigate this aspect more thoroughly.

The results for the 14 mm rope fitted with three 16 mm grips indicated 4 out of 5 specimens broke at the highest torque used instead of slipping. It is possible therefore that these grips could have reached the rope breaking load at lower torques, and this would have produced a slightly steeper slope to the line. It is of particular interest to note that, in this case, using 16 mm grips on a 14 mm rope gave a higher efficiency than when the same grips were used on a 16 mm rope. This feature is probably due to the higher stresses induced into the 14 mm rope under the U bolt of a 16 mm grip at the same torque value. This result does not mean that oversize grips would give generally higher efficiencies because a larger grip would also allow the rope to distort to an oval shape under the U bolt as it beds in and under dynamic loading - thus possibly allowing a dramatic reduction in the torque over a period of time. It is also relevant to note that previous work at HSE/RLSD on Crosby rope grips used in similar terminations showed that when used on a 22 mm diameter rope oversized (26 mm) grips gave reduced efficiencies when compared with terminations made with the correct 22 mm grips.

The results with five grips in each termination (Fig.19) as expected gave higher efficiencies with all three rope sizes checked but only the 13mm size approached the target 80% efficiency at the top end of practical torque values for this size of grip i.e. about 25 lbf.ft (33 Nm). With the 19 mm and 16 mm grips at practical torques of 35 - 40 lbf.ft (47 - 54 Nm) and 30 - 35 lbf.ft (40 - 47 Nm) the efficiencies were about 45% and 35% respectively.

The overall pattern of the results from this phase indicates that termination efficiencies at practical torque values for each size of rope are higher with the smaller ropes than with the larger ones. This programme was however restricted to ropes between 9 mm and 19 mm in diameter because the available test rig could not accommodate the length of specimen required for ropes over 19 mm. A limited series of tests carried out by HSE/RLSD in 1983 using three 22 mm Crosby rope grips on a 22mm rope also gave very low termination efficiencies because of the difficulty of applying adequate torque under service conditions without the aid of powered torque wrenches. It is the opinion of the author that terminations made up using BS 462 grips on larger ropes than those used in this programme would also give low termination efficiencies in most situations because of the problem of applying adequate torque values.

PHASE 5 - Wear Effects

The aim of this phase was to study the effects of using grips with worn bridges on the slip loads of the terminations.

The bridges on BS 462 grips are manufactured with several shallow ridges in their rope grooves. During service these ridges gradually get worn away by the pressures exerted by the rope wires on them, especially if the grips are removed and reset many times or if there is any slippage of the rope through the grips. It was intended therefore to investigate the effects of this wear on the slip load of the termination by repeating earlier tests but with the ridges machined smooth to simulate the worst possible condition likely to be met in service. Unfortunately this reprofiling of the bridge grooves proved totally impractical for it was found that the thickness of the bridge material after machining was insufficient to survive the bending stresses generated during tightening and all the modified bridges split across the rope groove whilst the nuts were being torqued up. As the amount of material removed in this reprofiling was relatively small it indicated that the thickness of the bridges given in BS 462: 1958 was barely adequate to survive the higher torques used in this programme. In practice however out of over 2000 BS 462 grips used in this programme only about five unmodified bridges failed, or distorted sufficiently to need replacing, whilst the nuts were being torqued up. After the tests at the higher torques a small number of the bridges had suffered sufficient permanent bending to prevent their re-use for any purpose.

Another feature of a grooved bridge is that if the ridges in the grooving are designed to fit a six strand rope they would not fit an eight strand, or any other construction, as effectively. The BS 462 grips purchased for this programme all had a ridge pattern in the bridge groove into which neither a six nor an eight strand rope would lie comfortably. In all cases the strand crowns pressed into the ridges at local high spots only, unless very high torques were used, and this caused rapid localised wear of the ridges. This feature was easily observed by looking through grips torqued up to different values and by studying the marks left by the strand crown wires on the bridge after each load test.

There are other types of wire rope grip which are similar to the BS 462 grips in having some form of ridges in their rope grooves e.g. Crosby grips, but another design, the DIN 1142 grip has a smooth groove. Differences between the effects of wear on these two basic designs is important. Wear in a smooth rope groove tends to cause slight roughening of the surface as the rope wires are pressed into it, developing a surface texture similar to a knurled finish. On the other hand with ridged grooves the effects of wear are to make the ridges progressively less prominent, reducing any interlocking effect they might have with the strands of the rope. Whatever the initial effect of the ridges, wear in service would be expected to alter the slip load characteristics of terminations made from such grips more than those made using grips with smooth bridges. In Phase 6 (see Part 3 of this paper) grips of different designs were compared and it is significant that the DIN 1142 grips with the smooth bridges outperformed all those with ridges in their rope grooves.

In view of the greatly superior performance of the DIN 1142 grip in these tests, and the relatively poor performance of the BS 462 grips, this phase of the work was put in abeyance until the results from the other phases had been assessed. It was later abandoned in the light of these other results. The only outcome from the preliminary work done was that it indicated that if any smoothing of existing ridges was to be attempted on the BS 462 design then bridges of a thicker section than that given in the 1958 and 1969 standards would be needed. For BS 462:1983 the bridge design was revised (at the behest of HSE/RLSD and NPL) to increase the thickness.

Since this programme of testing was completed grips purporting to be made to

BS 462:1983 have become available. A few tests were carried out in 1992 to see if there was any substantial improvement in the termination efficiency with these grips. Although the overall performance of the new grips was only slightly better than that of the earlier ones, due primarily to the poor quality of the U bolts, the design of the bridges had been improved for they were both thicker and had re-designed ridges in the rope groove which allowed a six strand rope to lie more comfortably in them. Seven tests with the new grips, and two tests using new grips with the ridges in the bridge grooves removed, gave slip loads which suggested that the ridged rope grooves in the new bridges contributed about 8% to the efficiency of a termination when using six strand rope. Ropes of constructions other than six strand would not lie comfortably across the new bridges however and therefore the termination efficiencies on these ropes would be lower.

PART 2 - SUMMARY

PHASE 2

The results from the tests in this phase were all influenced by the problem of how to measure the torque on the nuts of the grips without effectively re-torquing each one slightly in the process. The problem was anticipated at the outset but the magnitude of the effect was larger than expected especially where frequent check measurements were made. This is a problem for the researcher however, not for the practical engineer in the field, for regular checking and re-torquing of the grips has been shown to be one of the most important factors in the use of this type of termination.

The first of the tests in this phase showed that even with unloaded terminations, i.e. after tightening up the grips the test specimens were left lying on the laboratory bench, there was an initial reduction in the torque on the grips caused by the gradual crushing of the rope core under each grip. This effect is more significant with fibre cored than with steel cored ropes. The reduction is greater with the lower torque values, presumably because at higher torques the initial compression in the core is greater, leaving less potential for further movement. Reductions in torque of up to 50% were measured at the lower torques and around 30% for the higher torques. There is a danger however that the higher torques used in this programme could cause damage to the fibre core and to the wires under the grips even when the rope is not loaded.

Much of this reduction of torque on the grips on a new rope occurs over the first few hours after a termination has been made but in these tests further significant falls occurred over the first three days. It was noted that the reduction in torque at the first check point was very similar whether the first measurement was made after one day or after one week. This suggests that most of the reduction occurred during the first few hours and then the torque values became semi-stable until the grips were disturbed by the action of taking the next torque measurements. This pattern was repeated after every torque measurement.

41

In the second part of this phase the effects of holding a static load for different relatively short periods of time with the grips torqued up to different values were studied. The difference between holding a load of 30 kN (the SWL for the rope if the static safety factor is taken to be 5) for 5 min, 1 hour, and 5 hours was negligible. The mean straight line graph from all these 27 tests showed an efficiency improvement however over the data obtained during the equivalent tests with a 10 min hold period in phase 1, effectively doubling the efficiency at low torques (e.g. 20 lbf.ft, 27 Nm) from 10% to 20%, and raising it from about 50% to about 57% at 80 lbf.ft (108 Nm). It is considered that the re-torquing of the grips, which was carried out before the slip load tests were made, was the most important factor in producing this increase in efficiency.

A very important feature was the development of slip in those specimens only torqued up to 30 lbf.ft (41 Nm) when a load equivalent to the SWL was hung on the rope. It should be recalled that during the phase 1 tests with 16mm grips torques of around 30 - 35 lbf.ft (41 - 47 Nm) were judged by experienced service engineers as being about the maximum torque which would be applied in practice in the field.

The rate of rope slip through a termination varies with time but once slip has commenced it appears to continue, even if at a very slow rate, over periods of weeks or months

.

Re-torquing the grips increases the termination efficiency. Re-torquing after the service load has been hung from the rope improves the initial termination efficiency and should always be practiced. For example, in these tests re-torquing the grips after the load had been hung on the rope reduced the rate of slip by a factor of ten in tests with initial torques of 20 lbf.ft (27 Nm).

Tests in which the rope was loaded to the SWL and then unloaded over 30 cycles had only a small effect on the torque on the grips. At the higher initial torques cycling the rope load had little effect on the termination efficiency. At the lower torques load cycling seemed to help bed in the ropes under the grips which produced higher efficiencies.

It should be noted that all the tests in this programme were carried out under static loading conditions. Investigations into failures of this type of termination in service have suggested that wire rope grip terminations are generally more susceptible to the effects of dynamic and impulsive loading.

In the opinion of the author it is only the very high safety factors required in passenger carrying lift installations in the UK that prevent more incidents occurring due to slippage of the grips. Tests carried out, both by the author and by other organisations, on several actual lift installations have all indicated that re-torquing was needed to restore the original termination efficiency i.e. they were operating with much reduced safety factors.

PHASE 3

Fibre cored ropes of different constructions all behaved in a similar manner but a steel cored rope gave higher efficiencies all through the range of torques used. At a torque of 30 lbf.ft (41 Nm) the termination efficiency of a 16 mm steel cored rope was about double that of 16 mm fibre cored ropes.

PHASE 4

The efficiencies of terminations made using the smaller sizes of the BS 462 grips were higher than those of the larger sizes.

Practical torque values which can be applied without damaging the rope are related to the rope size. Although with the smaller sizes of grip the physical effort required to apply the torque is not a problem there are practical difficulties of holding the grips to stop them twisting and damaging the rope whilst the torque is being applied.

PHASE 5

Wear effects on BS 462 grips could not be fully investigated because the bridges on the grips used in the main programme proved to be too weak to allow any re-profiling of the rope grooves. Tests in 1992 using grips purporting to be made to BS 462:1983, which were not available when the main programme was carried out, indicated that well designed ridged bridge grooves could contribute an extra 8% or thereabouts to the termination efficiency over bridges with smooth grooves but only when used with the type of ropes for which they had been designed. Bridges with smooth rope grooves had the advantage that their performance was unaffected by wear and they could be used with different rope constructions.

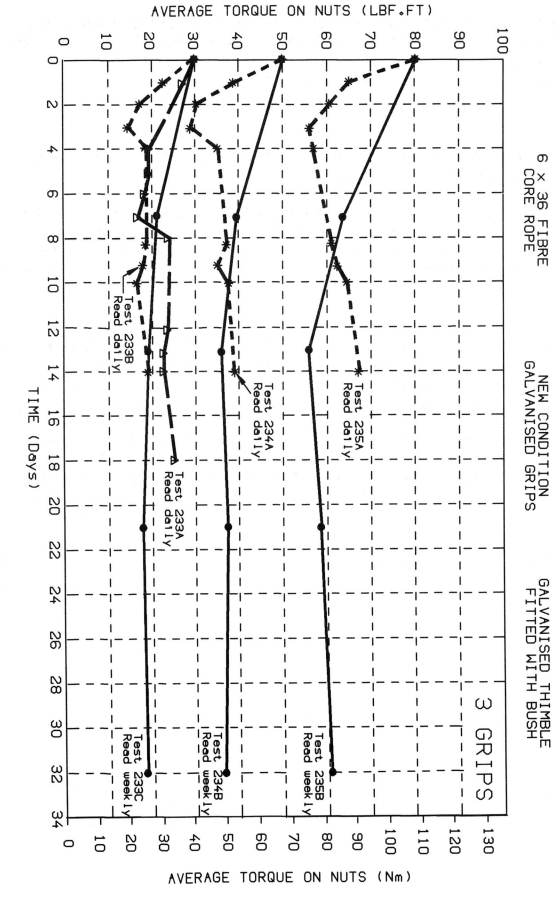

Fig.8 Loss of torque v. Time under no load conditions

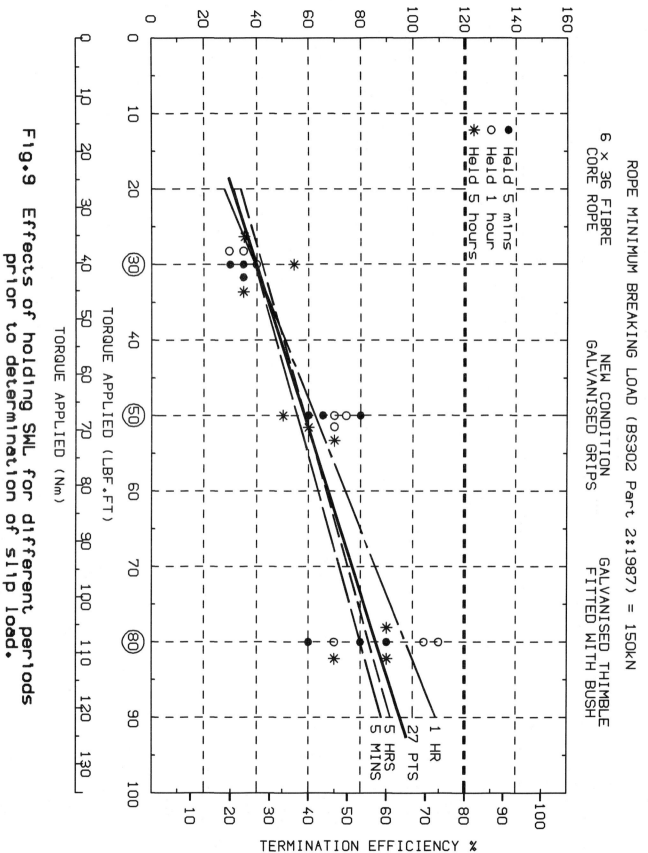

Fig.9 Effects of holding SWL for different periods prior to determination of slip load.

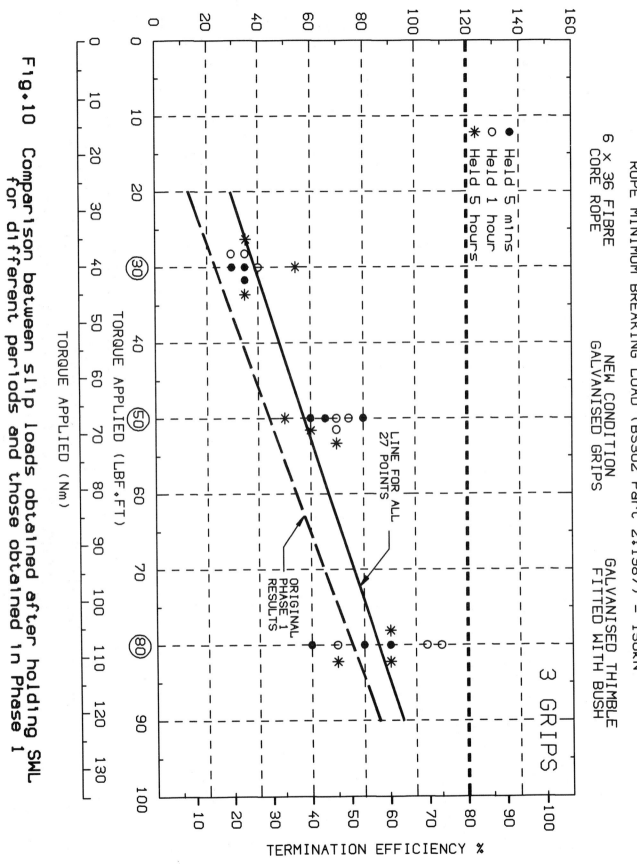

BS462 16mm WIRE ROPE GRIPS

ROPE MINIMUM BREAKING LOAD (BS302 Part 2:1987) = 150kN

6 × 36 FIBRE
CORE ROPE

NEW CONDITION
GALVANISED GRIPS

GALVANISED THIMBLE
FITTED WITH BUSH

3 GRIPS

● Held 5 mins
○ Held 1 hour
✱ Held 5 hours

LINE FOR ALL
27 POINTS

ORIGINAL
PHASE 1
RESULTS

Fig.10 Comparison between slip loads obtained after holding SWL
for different periods and those obtained in Phase 1

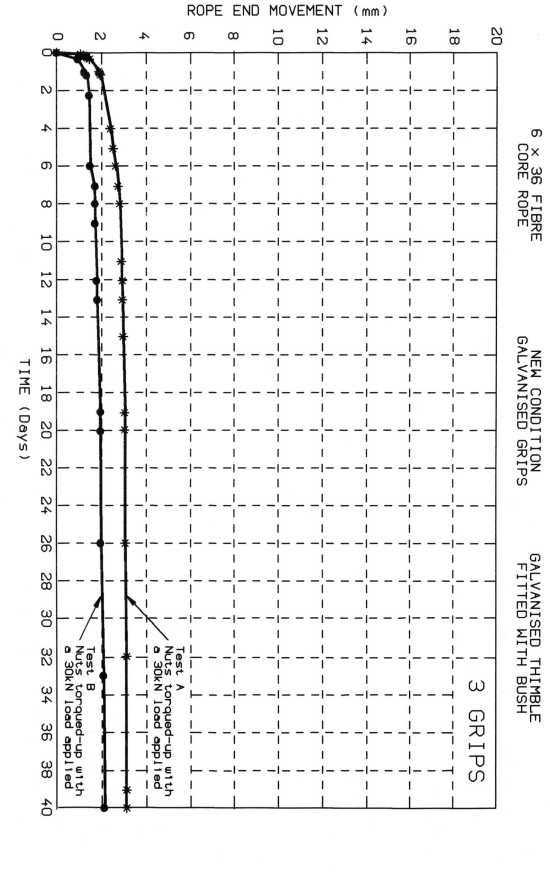

BS462 16mm WIRE ROPE GRIPS

6 x 36 FIBRE
CORE ROPE

NEW CONDITION
GALVANISED GRIPS

GALVANISED THIMBLE
FITTED WITH BUSH

3 GRIPS

ROPE END MOVEMENT (mm)

TIME (Days)

Test A
Nuts torqued-up with
a 30kN load applied

Test B
Nuts torqued-up with
a 30kN load applied

Fig.11 Slip v. Time whilst holding a load of 30kN
Initial torque: 30 lbf.ft (41Nm)

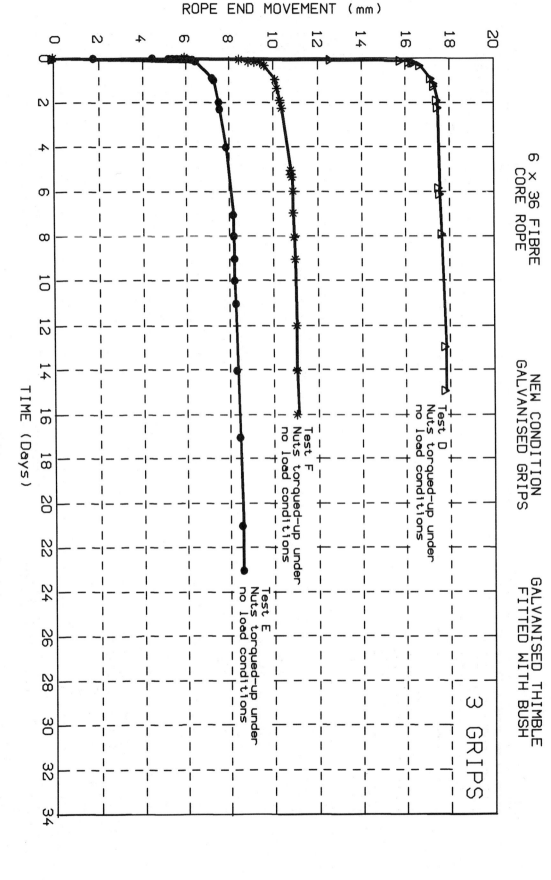

BS462 16mm WIRE ROPE GRIPS

6 × 36 FIBRE
CORE ROPE

NEW CONDITION
GALVANISED GRIPS

GALVANISED THIMBLE
FITTED WITH BUSH

3 GRIPS

ROPE END MOVEMENT (mm)

TIME (Days)

Test D
Nuts torqued-up under
no load conditions

Test F
Nuts torqued-up under
no load conditions

Test E
Nuts torqued-up under
no load conditions

Fig.12   Slip v. Time whilst holding a load of 30kN
Initial torque: 25 lbf.ft (34Nm)

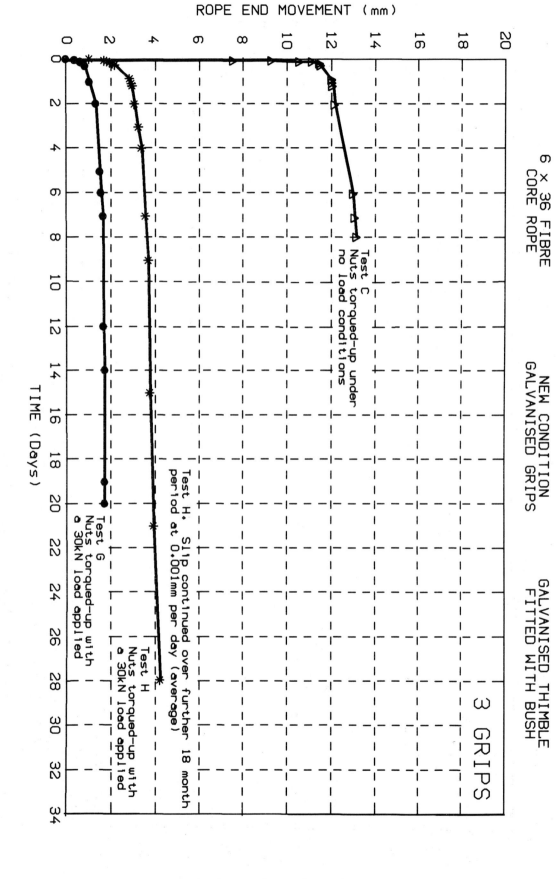

BS462 16mm WIRE ROPE GRIPS

6 × 36 FIBRE
CORE ROPE

NEW CONDITION
GALVANISED GRIPS

GALVANISED THIMBLE
FITTED WITH BUSH

3 GRIPS

ROPE END MOVEMENT (mm)

TIME (Days)

Test C
Nuts torqued-up under
no load conditions

Test H. Slip continued over further 18 month
period at 0.001mm per day (average)

Test G
Nuts torqued-up with
a 30kN load applied

Test H
Nuts torqued-up with
a 30kN load applied

Fig.13   Slip v. Time whilst holding a load of 30kN
Initial torque: 20 lbf.ft (27Nm)

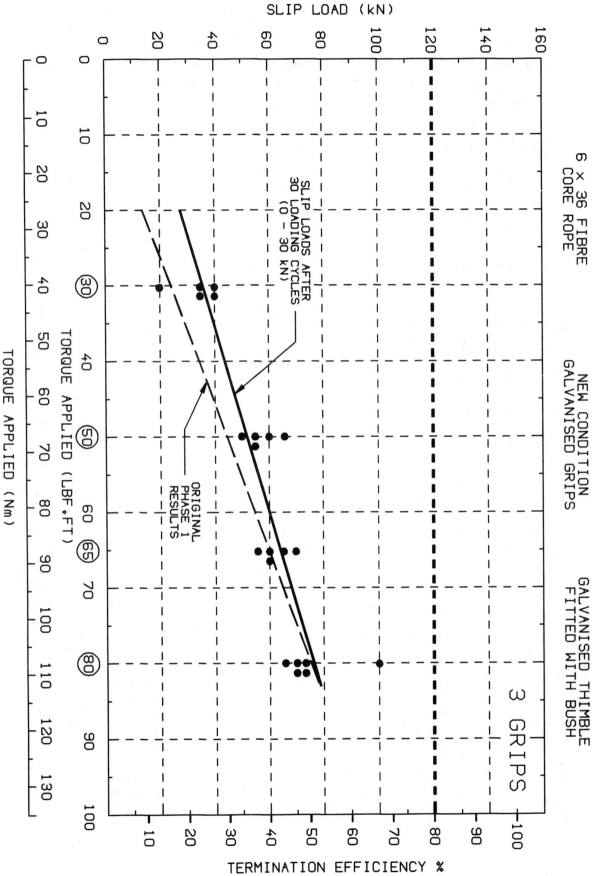

Fig.14 Slip Load v. Initial Torque after 30 load cycles

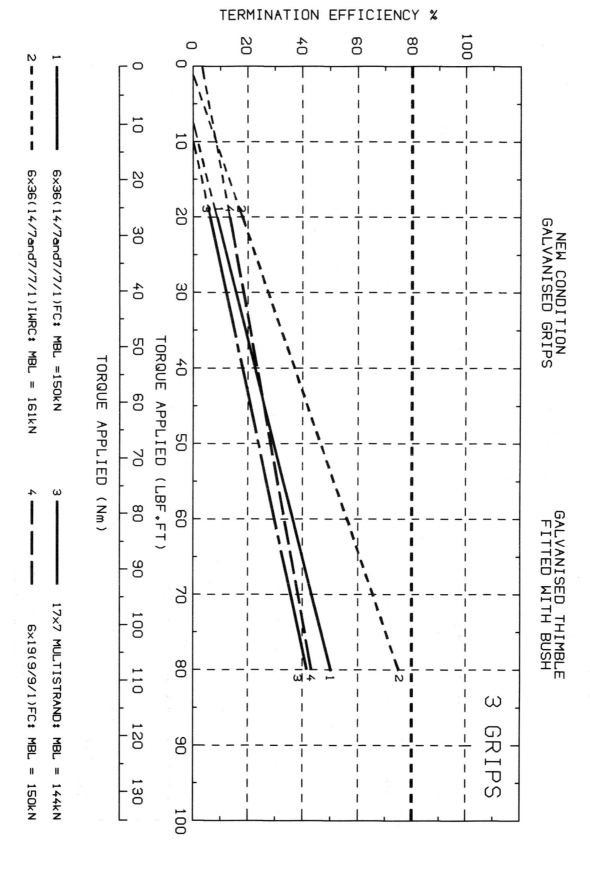

BS462 16mm WIRE ROPE GRIPS

NEW CONDITION
GALVANISED GRIPS

GALVANISED THIMBLE
FITTED WITH BUSH

3 GRIPS

TERMINATION EFFICIENCY %

TORQUE APPLIED (LBF.FT)

TORQUE APPLIED (Nm)

1 ——— 6×36(14/7and7/7/1)FC; MBL =150kN

2 ------ 6×36(14/7and7/7/1)IWRC; MBL = 161kN

3 ——— 17×7 MULTISTRAND; MBL = 144kN

4 ——— 6×19(9/9/1)FC; MBL = 150kN

**Fig.15 3 Grip Termination Efficiency v. Initial Torque
for different rope constructions**

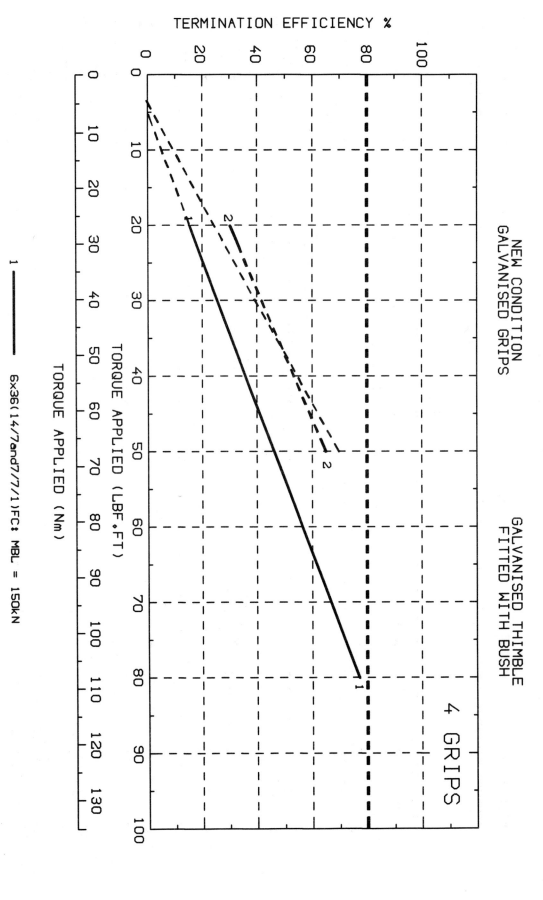

Fig.16   4 Grip Termination Efficiency v. Initial Torque
          for different rope constructions

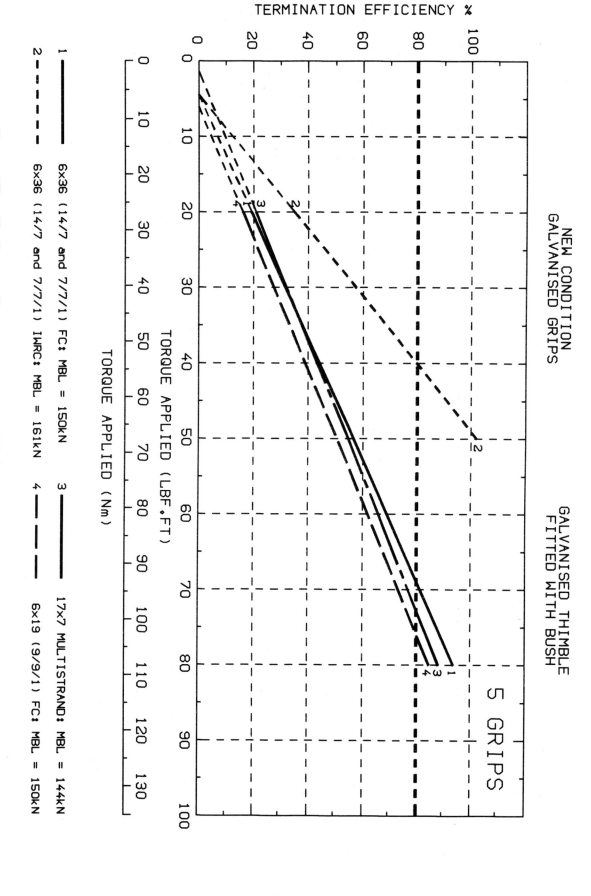

Fig.17 5 Grip Termination Efficiency v. Initial Torque
for different rope constructions

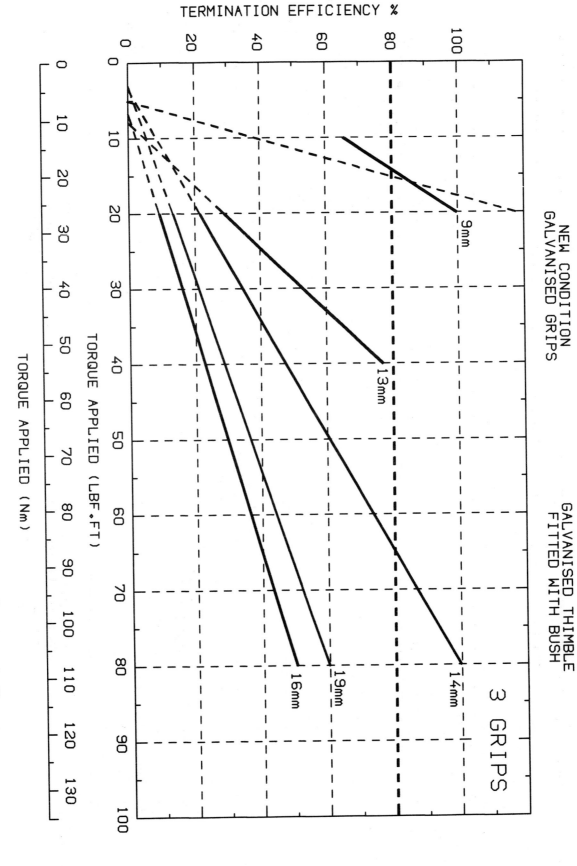

BS462 WIRE ROPE GRIPS

ROPE CONSTRUCTION: 6x36(14/7and7/7/1)FC

NEW CONDITION
GALVANISED GRIPS

GALVANISED THIMBLE
FITTED WITH BUSH

3 GRIPS

TERMINATION EFFICIENCY %

TORQUE APPLIED (LBF.FT)

TORQUE APPLIED (Nm)

Fig.18 3 Grip Termination Efficiency v. Initial Torque
for ropes of different sizes

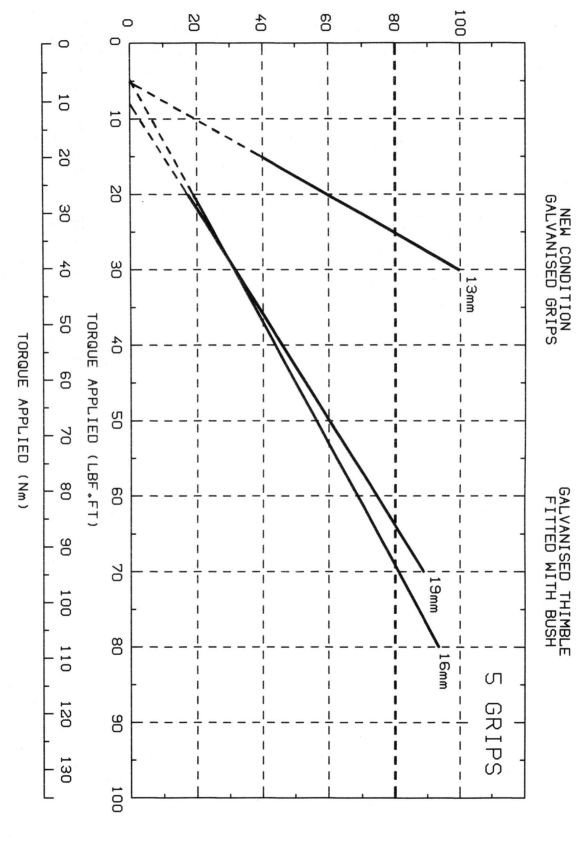

BS462 WIRE ROPE GRIPS

ROPE CONSTRUCTION: 6x36(14/7and7/7/1)FC

NEW CONDITION
GALVANISED GRIPS

GALVANISED THIMBLE
FITTED WITH BUSH

5 GRIPS

TERMINATION EFFICIENCY %

TORQUE APPLIED (LBF.FT)

TORQUE APPLIED (Nm)

13mm

19mm

16mm

Fig.19 5 Grip Termination Efficiency v. Initial Torque
for ropes of different sizes

PART 3

The first two parts of this paper concentrated on the performance of terminations made using BS 462 wire rope grips. They included discussions of results from tests to study the effects of different torques, different numbers of grips per termination, different rope constructions, different rope sizes, and the effects of time on the residual torque on the grips. In this, the concluding part, comparison tests between BS 462 grips and some of the alternative types of grip generally available in the UK are discussed. The paper includes a general discussion and conclusions from the whole programme and makes some recommendations with regard to the use of terminations presently made with BS 462 wire rope grips in the UK with special emphasis on passenger carrying installations.

It should be noted that as a result of the research reported in this paper BS 462 was eventually withdrawn in 1991. Large numbers of grips purporting to have been made to BS 462 remain in service however and will continue to be used for many years.

A new European CEN Standard for wire rope grips for eye terminations has been drafted, this was issued for public comment in 1994. DIN 1142 was used as the basis for this draft standard.

RESULTS AND DISCUSSION OF TESTS (Continued from Part 2)

PHASE 6 - Comparisons with Alternative Designs

In this part of the programme the results obtained in Phase 1 using BS 462 grips were compared with those obtained from tests under identical conditions using some of the alternative designs of grip which are commercially available in the UK.

The grips chosen for these comparison tests are shown in Fig.20. It should be noted that all the alternative designs tested had either a galvanised, or a zinc electroplated and chromatised finish.

In general only a few tests were carried out on each design of grip so that approximate comparisons could be made between their performance and that of BS 462 grips. It was not the intention to carry out comprehensive tests on all these designs but just sufficient to obtain a general guide to their performance under as near identical conditions as possible.

All the tests were carried out on 16 mm diameter 6x36FC rope, as used in Phase 1, using the same test method, the same test rig, and the same instrumentation as that used for the BS 462 tests. In the cases where the grip manufacturer recommended the numbers of grips, and the torque values to be applied for ropes of different sizes, terminations using these were tested. In addition tests were also made where relevant with terminations made up using three grips torqued up to 40 lbf.ft (54 Nm) for a more direct comparison with the BS 462 grips at what the author considered was a more practicable torque than those recommended by some manufacturers. None of the grips were supplied with loose washers so none were fitted for these tests.

The detailed results from the tests in this phase are given in Figs.21-27.

Crosby rope clips

Eleven tests were made using three clips in each rope termination as recommended for this size of rope by Crosby on their instruction sheet for fitters.

The first three tests were carried out according to the fitting instructions from Crosby but using tightening torques of 100 lbf.ft (136 Nm) instead of the 95 lbf.ft (129 Nm) actually recommended by Crosby. This slight increase was necessary because the torque wrench used for this work was not marked at 95 lbf.ft, so for consistency the nearest higher mark was used. This 100 lbf.ft (136 Nm) torque was initially applied with a small load of 3kN applied to the rope but in accordance with the Crosby instructions it was checked at the working load, in this case assumed to be 30 kN - the maximum safe working load for the rope. The manufacturer's fitting instructions state that the threads of the U bolts and nuts should be clean, dry and free from lubrication so they were tested in this condition. In all three cases the rope eventually broke under the grip furthest from the thimble at loads of 137 kN, 137 kN, and 140 kN i.e. at around 90% efficiency. The initial failure occurring at points

58

where the wires on the live side had been deeply nicked either by pressure from the crown wires on the tail side, or by inter-strand pressures generated between adjacent strands on the live side due to distortion caused by the tail side pressing into it.

Even before the tests it was apparent however that the high applied torque was causing severe distortion and damage in the ropes under the grips. The pressure from the U bolts on the tail side of the ropes caused very deep indentations and damaged several wires under each hoop. There was also a lot of distortion and deep nicking damage to individual strand crown wires where the two parts of the rope were pressed together under each grip. Examination after the tests revealed that the fibre main cores had been chopped, or badly damaged, under each grip, but these samples had been subjected to loads of 90% or more of the MBL of the rope during the tests so both the torque and the load would have contributed to this damage.

The application of a torque as high as 95 or 100 lbf.ft (129 or 136 Nm) for a 16 mm rope termination was very difficult to achieve even in the laboratory because of the physical effort involved. In the opinion of the author, to apply such a torque under many service conditions would necessitate the use of a power tool. It is the opinion of the author therefore that although the recommended torque produced a termination efficiency of about 90%, meeting the manufacturer's claims, it is impractical to use such a torque because of the difficulty in applying it in many situations unless power tools are available, and because of the damage it does to the rope under the grips.

In view of the above findings eight further tests were carried out at a torque of 40 lbf.ft (54 Nm). This is the maximum torque which it seemed practical to apply on 16 mm grips, in the opinion of the author, with regard to the physical effort required and to avoid distortion related damage. Four of the tests were made after the torque had been applied with a small holding load of 3 kN on the rope. In the other four tests the torque was first applied with a load of 3 kN on the rope but then the load was increased to 30 kN, the maximum SWL for this rope assuming a Factor of Safety (FOS) of 5, and the nuts retorqued to 40 lbf.ft (54 Nm). The results of these eight tests are shown on Fig.21. The four tests, where the grips had been re-torqued after the higher load had been applied, gave a slightly higher average slip load (77.5 kN) than the tests where the grips had been torqued up at a load of only 3 kN (average slip load 70 kN), i.e. the mean efficiencies were about 52% and 47% respectively, so the effect of re-torquing the nuts after the SWL had been applied to the rope was to increase the termination efficiency by about 5%.

Although these limited tests showed that the often quoted 80% efficiency for this type of termination was met on this 16 mm diameter rope if the manufacturer's recommended torque was applied, they also highlighted the fact that at more practical torque values, which could be achieved without the use of power tools, the efficiency was much lower at about 50%. The results also illustrate that when the nuts are re-torqued after a higher load has been applied to the rope, the termination efficiencies will be increased by up to 5%. There would also be a smaller loss of torque during the test for the higher load stretches the rope more which helps to bed down the strands.

The tests did not establish a torque value at which the termination efficiency was just sufficient to break the rope but, in my opinion, it could be appreciably below the Crosby recommended value of 95 lbf.ft (129 Nm), possibly as low as 75 - 80 lbf.ft (102 - 108 Nm). If a linear relationship between torque and slip load is assumed, as with the BS 462 grips, then a line drawn through the zero load at zero torque point (this makes no allowance for any loss of torque due to friction between the threads at low loads) and through the mean of the eight test points at 40 lbf.ft (54 Nm), i.e. approx 73.8 kN or 49% efficiency, should give a very rough guide to the torque v. efficiency performance. Such a line has been drawn on Fig.21. If only the four results from the samples torqued up at 3 kN are considered - a more correct comparison with the BS 462 grip tests - then the mean slip load was 70 kN, i.e. 47% efficiency, which indicates that terminations made with three Crosby grips had efficiencies about double those of terminations made with three galvanised BS 462 grips at 40 lbf.ft (54 Nm) torque. Further testing would be necessary to establish this relationship with any accuracy over a range of torque values.

Torque measurements made after the completion of each test indicated a mean reduction in torque of about 44% from the 40 lbf.ft (54 Nm) setting up level but as with the BS 462 grips there was a very wide scatter in the residual torque on individual nuts. It was not possible to check the residual torque in the tests which were carried out at 100 lbf.ft (136 Nm) because of the effects on the termination of the rope breaking.

The Crosby fitting instructions state that their tightening torque values are based upon the threads being clean, dry, and free from lubrication. The note that the threads should not be lubricated is based on the philosophy that it would be difficult to ensure fitters always greased the threads whilst assembling the grips and therefore it is safer to assume the worst case applies, i.e. the threads are not lubricated, and to use a high torque value to compensate for the increased friction losses. By applying a high torque the reduction of torque with time would still leave adequate strength in the termination to reduce the necessity to re-torque in service.

In the light of the results from this programme of tests it is the opinion of the author that if the threads were greased before use then appreciably lower torque values than those recommended, could be used whilst still achieving an 80% efficiency. The lower torques, possibly around 65 lbf.ft (88 Nm) would be easier to apply and less damaging to the rope. If for a 16 mm rope the termination included a fourth grip, i.e one more than the present recommended minimum number, then even lower torques would be needed to achieve 80% efficiency. Tests at high torques using BS 462 grips in Phase 2 of this programme indicated that on fibre cored ropes the reduction of torque with time was less than in tests at lower initial torques but it was still around 30%. The reduction of torque on Crosby grips would probably follow a similar pattern so even though the residual torque would be still relatively high there would be a corresponding reduction in efficiency from the initial value. Retorquing would then be necessary if the original efficiency was to be maintained.

DIN 1142 wire rope grips

The DIN 1142 Standard recommends the use of four grips on a 16 mm diameter rope, one more than the minimum originally recommended in BS 462. Tests were therefore carried out with terminations made using both three and four grips. The three grip tests being a better comparison against the same numbers of grips of other designs, whilst the four grip tests followed the DIN recommendations.

Seven tests were made with three grip terminations, in two the threads were left as supplied with just a trace of grease left on the threads from manufacture, and in the other five the threads were properly greased before assembly on the rope as recommended in DIN 1142. In all seven cases only the recommended torque 49 Nm (36 lbf.ft) was applied for this value seemed realistic in that it could be put on in service without too much difficulty, it did not appear to cause any excessive damage to the rope, and it was very similar to the upper limit of the torques put on BS 462 grips by experienced fitters. The results of these tests are shown in Fig.22.

As with the BS 462 tests, grips with greased threads gave higher efficiencies than those which remained as supplied i.e. almost ungreased. The increase due to greasing the threads seemed to be up to about 10% but this figure was calculated from very few data points.

The initial four grip termination torqued up to 36 lbf.ft (49 Nm) at a low load of 3 kN only was strong enough to break the rope at 150 kN, its stated minimum breaking load. It was decided therefore not to re-torque after the working load (assumed to be a SWL of 30 kN for this rope in these tests) had been applied although this is required by the DIN 1142 Standard. This omission represents the worst situation which might arise in service but it made the results more directly comparable with those carried out using BS 462 grips in phase 1 of this programme. Tests in other parts of the programme in which other designs of grip were re-torqued at the SWL indicated termination efficiencies increased by around 5%, so the requirement to re-torque grips immediately after the service load is applied for the first time, which is included in the DIN 1142 Standard and in several alternative grip manufacturers' fitting instructions, is a beneficial feature.

The mean efficiency for a termination using three DIN 1142 grips was approximately 75% with greased threads and 65% with ungreased threads, whereas the efficiency of terminations using three galvanised BS 462 grips with ungreased threads under the same torque conditions was approximately 20%, and that of three ungalvanised BS 462 grips with ungreased threads approximately 48%.

Approximately 40 tests were made with four DIN 1142 grip terminations. The tests were carried out in four groups with a different batch of grips for each group. In each test the grips were torqued up to the recommended 36 lbf.ft (49 Nm) but at a low load of about 3 kN only - the results are shown in Fig.23 (first group, first load cycle only) and Fig.24.

With the first batch of grips five tests out of eight resulted in the rope breaking. Slip at lower loads was recorded in the other three tests (Fig.23). The lowest slip occurred at 100 kN (67% efficiency), this specimen was then unloaded and retested without retorquing - on this second load cycle slip was detected at 105 kN (Fig.24). This specimen was then unloaded again, retorqued to 36 lbf.ft (49 Nm) and retested - on this occasion the rope broke at 150 kN without any detectable slip as shown in Figs.24 (Columns 1/1-1/3) illustrating the benefit of re-torquing.

Following the good results obtained with the first batch of grips another batch was purchased from the same supplier. The results of the tests on these grips is shown in Fig.24 (Column 2/1) - surprisingly slip was detected in all the tests at relatively low loads which gave a mean efficiency of only around 46% for grips with greased threads (5 tests) and about 20% for ungreased threads (1 test) Although most of the test specimens with grips from the second batch had been assembled by an inexperienced fitter, who had not been previously used for this work, the specimens appeared identical with those made up by the experienced fitter using the first batch of grips. In all these tests the torques had been applied by the person who carried out most of the programme. The same torque meter was used for all torques below 90 lbf.ft, its operating limit, and its calibration was checked at intervals throughout the work. Examination of the DIN grips revealed no difference between this batch, the first batch and the two batches supplied later - all conformed to the current DIN 1142 Standard.

Immediately after the detection of slip in four of the above tests the specimens were unloaded and then re-torqued to 36 lbf.ft (49 Nm) and retested - the results are shown if Fig.24 (Column 2/2). In each case the second loading cycle produced an increase of about 25% in the load at which slip began.

At a later date three further tests were made using grips from batch 2. These grips had all been used in one previous test but they showed very little damage to either the hoops or the bridge pieces. In this case the specimens were assembled by the experienced fitter who had made up the specimens with the first batch of DIN grips and most of the other tests specimens in this programme. The results are shown in Fig.24 (Column 2/3). The three tests gave slip initiation loads of 80, 90, and 130 kN, i.e. efficiencies of 53, 60, and 87% respectively.

No satisfactory explanation has been found for the relatively low efficiencies obtained in the first tests with the second batch of grips. The calibrations of the load cell and the torque meter were checked and shown to be accurate and consistent throughout. Hardness measurements on the grips from the different batches indicated no significant differences. As all the specimens made up using the DIN grips looked similar it seems inconceivable that the experience or inexperience of the two fitters played a significant role.

Following the large differences obtained with the first two batches of grips two further batches were purchased from the same supplier. The results from tests made using these grips are shown in Fig.24 (Columns 3 and 4). These show slip initiation loads or rope break points very similar to those obtained with the first batch of grips. The range of efficiencies for the terminations varied from over 90% (rope break points) to as low as 60% but all these were well above the 32% efficiency which the performance graphs (Fig.4, also shown of Fig.23) indicate could have been obtained using four BS 462 galvanised grips at the same torque value.

DIN 1142 four grip terminations were also tested on the 16 mm Lang's lay 17x7 multistrand rope used in the BS 462 grip tests. After being torqued up to 36 lbf.ft (49 Nm) slip initiation points were obtained at 70, 90, and 95 kN i.e. 49, 62, and 66% efficiencies (based on MBL = 144 kN for this rope) which give a mean value of 59%, see Fig.24 (Column 5). Four grip BS 462 terminations were not tested on this rope so no direct comparison is possible. Tests on three and five galvanised grip BS 462 terminations were made however and, from the slip v. torque graphs, a torque of 36 lbf.ft (49 Nm) would have held the rope up to 24 kN and 56 kN respectively i.e termination efficiencies of 17% and 39% respectively. On the basis of these results and assuming approximate linearity a four grip BS 462 termination might have had an efficiency of about 28% on this rope. <u>If this value is accepted then the DIN grip terminations gave approximately double the efficiency of terminations with the same number of BS 462 grips on this multistrand rope</u>
.

<u>Generally these DIN 1142 grips gave efficiencies appreciably higher than BS 462 grips under similar conditions. The torque recommended for 16 mm DIN 1142 grips was achievable in practice with a reasonable amount of physical effort and it did not cause any serious distortion or damage to the rope.</u> One set of these grips however gave much lower efficiency values, especially when used with ungreased threads, for which there was no apparent reason. In three tests on a Lang's lay multistrand rope the efficiencies, although above those for BS 462 grips, were appreciably lower than the mean values obtained on 6x36 FC rope.

DIN 1142 grips, like BS 462 grips, showed a reduction in torque with time, and after a load had been applied to the rope, indicating that they required re-torquing at intervals during the service life of each termination. The reduction in torque at the completion of the first cycle tests was in the range 26% to 56%, with a mean value of about 40%. This is similar to that measured with the BS 462 and Crosby grips but this is not surprising for this reduction comes basically from the crushing of the main core of the rope rather than the actual grip design. After re-torquing and carrying out a second slip load test on the same termination the reduction in torque after the second cycle was in the range 25% to 40% with a mean value about 35%, i.e. slightly less than after the first cycle.

It should also be re-emphasised that the tests on the DIN 1142 grips were carried out after the torque had been applied whilst there was only a small tension in the rope. If the grips had been re-torqued, as instructed in the DIN 1142 Standard, after the service load, or the SWL in this case, had been applied for the first time then results obtained in other parts of this programme suggest that the termination efficiencies would have been increased by about 5%.

Fist grips

Crosby, the manufacturer of the Fist grip, states on its technical information sheet for Fist grips, that the minimum number of these grips which should be used for a termination on a 16 mm diameter rope is three, and they recommend a tightening torque of 130 lbf.ft (177 Nm). There was no reference in the manufacturer's original fitting instructions, supplied with the grips, to greasing the threads before fitting the grips on the rope so the initial tests were carried out with the grips as supplied i.e. with ungreased threads. In a later (1989) information brochure Crosby states that their recommended torques are based upon the threads being clean, dry, and free from lubrication.

The recommended torque of 130 lbf.ft (177 Nm) proved very difficult to apply in practice even with the aid of a torque wrench with an extra long handle. Two persons were needed to do this, one to hold one of the nuts whilst the second applied the torque to the other. In the opinion of the author, to achieve this level of torque regularly in practice the use of a power tool would be essential.

In the first six tests the recommended torque was applied and checked as required at the working load, in this case assumed to be 30 kN i.e. the SWL of the rope assuming a Factor of Safety (FOS) of 5. Four tests were made with ungreased threads and two with greased threads, see Fig.25. In both the tests with greased threads the rope broke under the grips furthest from the thimble at termination efficiencies over 90%. The four tests with ungreased threads gave efficiencies between 80% and 47%, mean 62%, so as with all the other types of grip tested in this programme greasing the threads gave a worthwhile increase in the termination efficiency. Three of the four tests with the ungreased threads did not meet the manufacturer's claimed 80% efficiency for this type of termination when the slip of the rope through the termination was determined as in this programme. Insufficient tests were made however for an accurate quantitative assessment of the effect of greasing to be made. At the end of these tests the reduction in the torque on the nuts was found to lie in range 37% to 63%, mean value 45%.

Later seven tests were made, four at torques of 80 lbf.ft (108 Nm), and three at 40 lbf.ft (54 Nm) in line with the torques used during the testing of the BS 462 grips. For the purpose of consistency and for comparison with the BS 462 grips the torques were applied with a nominal load of 3 kN as in the BS 462 tests. At these low torques the efficiencies of the terminations were slightly less than half those of terminations made using three galvanised BS 462 grips (Fig.25). The reduction in the torque measured after each test was found to be about 40% for the nuts originally torqued to 80 lbf.ft (108 Nm) and 25% for those originally torqued to 40 lbf.ft (54 Nm).

The very limited number of tests on this type of grip showed that at the very high torque value recommended, terminations made up using three grips could give efficiencies of over 80% but probably only if the threads were greased before use. Using grips with ungreased threads, as supplied, and more practical torque values gave very low termination efficiencies. As with other designs of grip there was an appreciable reduction in the torque on the nuts after a load had been applied to the

64

termination. This suggests that regular re-torquing during service would be essential to maintain the termination efficiency.

A beneficial feature of this grip was that because of its double bridge design the grips did not cause as much distortion to the rope as those designs which use a U bolt, even when the very high recommended torques were used. The grips are not "handed" and therefore they can be put on a rope either way round.

Iron Wire Rope Grips

The supplier of these grips provided a brochure which gave details of the grips and the rope sizes on which they could be fitted. This brochure gave no information about the fitting of the grips e.g. the numbers to be used on different ropes, the torques to be applied, or about greasing the threads before use. Consequently to simplify comparison with other designs three grips were chosen together with a galvanised BS 464 thimble for each termination on the 16 mm 6x36 FC rope used in other parts of this programme.

The grips were initially used as supplied, i.e. without greasing the threads (9 tests), but later seven tests were also made with greased threads.

In this design the two halves of the grip are held together by two separate bolts and nuts, the head of each bolt fitting into a small hexagonal recess in one half of the grip. These recesses effectively stop the heads of the bolts from rotating whilst the nuts are being tightened but they also prevent a spanner being put on the heads to help to hold the bolt during tightening. Because the outside profile of the grip is relatively smooth and its corners are rounded off, it is difficult to hold the grip whilst tightening the nuts, with the result that the main reaction to the applied torque has to be provided by the rope itself. Care needs to be taken therefore not to damage the rope adjacent to each grip during the torquing process.

In these tests the torque was applied with a nominal load of 3 kN on the rope, as in the tests on the BS 462 grips. At the higher torques used it was found that the grips twisted appreciably on the rope whilst they were being torqued up and there was some concern about the distortion this caused in the rope between the grips. Actually applying the torque to the nuts of these grips also caused some difficulty because the nuts were of a much smaller size than those used on most of the other designs of grips for a 16 mm rope, consequently it was considered essential to use either a ring spanner or a socket spanner to avoid damaging the nuts.

The torque used for the first test was 40 lbf.ft (54 Nm) as this seemed about the maximum practical value for in service use based on experience with BS 462 grips. The results of the test are shown in Fig.26. The tests at 40 lbf.ft with ungreased threads gave very low efficiencies - about 13%. Raising the torque to 60 lbf.ft (81 Nm) and 80 lbf.ft (108 Nm) lifted the mean efficency to about 40% and 65% respectively but these torques seemed much too high to apply in service because of the difficulty of holding the grips mentioned above.

The design of these grips was such that they did much less damage to the ropes, and the fibre cores in particular, than those designs which used U bolts, e.g. BS 462, Crosby and DIN 1142 grips. It was noted however that several of the fibre cores had been partly severed under some of the grips after the completion of the tests but it is considered more likely that this damage was caused by the extension of the rope whilst under high load during the tests than to the crushing effect of these grips.

When the threads of the bolts were greased before use the efficiency of the termination was dramatically increased - by a factor of five at a torque of 40 lbf.ft (54 Nm) and by a factor of over two at 60 lbf.ft (81 Nm), see Fig.26.

During these tests the loss of torque on the nuts varied over a wide range, there being a slightly larger fall with greased threads (mean 39%) than with ungreased threads (mean 32%). The highest loads reached in the tests caused a reduction of about 40%, whilst in the tests which were stopped at much lower loads the reduction was nearer to 30%. These values are very similar to those obtained with other designs of grip.

Although only a small number of tests were carried out it seemed that this design of grip caused less damage to the rope than those which include U bolts. At torque values that were considered to be practical for use under service conditions the essential need to grease the threads was clearly illustrated. The difference in efficiency between terminations using these grips with greased and ungreased bolts was very significant - it is thought that this was probably related to the smaller diameter bolts used in this design. It could give rise to considerable variations in performance in service.

Eureka Wire Locks

Single Eureka Wire-Locks are said to be capable of holding ropes up to the Minimum Breaking Loads (MBL) of the ropes without failing. In the UK agent's brochure the unit shown as supplied for 16 mm rope is clamped together with four Allen cap-head screws of 12 mm diameter (Fig.20). In practice the units supplied for a 16 mm diameter rope were stamped 15/16 mm and the two halves were pulled together by two screws of 12 mm diameter. All the Eureka units above the 16 mm size have four screws, and those below 15 mm two screws, but it appears that at the time these tests were being made there were two models available for 16 mm ropes. All the tests done at this time were made using the two screw model. The manufacturer supplied recommended torques values for each size of grip, for the 16 mm unit this is 83.2 lbf.ft (113 Nm). This value was used for all the tests. All the screw threads were greased before use as recommended by the UK agent.

The results of five tests, each using a single Eureka grip, are shown in Fig.27. The mean efficiency obtained was 45%, with individual values ranging from 37% to 57%. Examination of the ropes and the Eureka grips after these tests revealed very little damage so each test specimen was retorqued and re-tested with the grip still in its original position on the rope. The results from the second cycle tests are included in

66

a separate column in Fig.27 - the mean efficiency obtained from the second cycle tests was 57%, with individual values ranging from 50% to 63%, i.e. an increase in mean slip load of 12%. Measurement of the torques on the bolts before and after each test revealed that after the first test the torques had dropped by an average of about 25% whereas after the second cycle the average reduction was about 17%. These results indicate the importance of re-torquing the screws at intervals with this type of grip.

Because of the relatively low efficiencies reached when using the recommended torque further tests at lower torques were not carried out. Athough the size and shape of this grip made it easier to hold than some of the other designs a torque of 83 lbf.ft (113 Nm) was difficult to apply in practice. The use of high strength Allen screws of relatively small diameter contributed to this difficulty. The length of these screws also caused some problems for it proved difficult to hold the two halves of the grip close enough together initially to engage the Allen screws in the tapped holes. At the completion of the tests several of the threads in the tapped holes had been damaged preventing the grips being used again.

In Finland, where it is reported that Eureka grips are fairly widely used, it is understood that these grips must be used in pairs (or greater numbers) for any lifting application. In such circumstances it is probable that termination efficiencies of 80% or more can be achieved at the recommended torques.

The alternative four screw version of the 16 mm grip would be expected to give a higher efficiency than the two screw version submitted for these tests. It might also survive a greater number of fittings than the two screw model.

Summary of results from Phase 6

In this phase the majority of the tests were carried out on 16 mm 6x36FC rope, comparisons between the different designs therefore may be only valid for this one size and construction. It is thought likely however that most designs would perform on other sizes and constructions in a similar manner to the BS 462 grips, e.g. the termination efficiencies would be higher on the smaller ropes and their performance on other fibre cored ropes would be similar to those obtained in these limited tests.

All the designs required nuts or screws to be tightened up to establish the initial grip. Measurement of the torques on the nuts and screws showed that with all designs there was a gradual reduction in torque with time and after a termination had been loaded. All the designs needed re-tightening at intervals if their initial termination efficiency was to be maintained.

Where the grip manufacturers had published recommended torques to achieve termination efficiencies of 80% or thereabouts these values seemed generally, with the exception of the single grip Eureka termination, to produce efficiencies of this order, but in some cases only when the threads were greased. The 80% efficiency point might have been reached by the four screw version of the 16 mm Eureka grip at the recommended torque but this version was not tested. However the actual torques recommended by the manufacturers were in most cases considered by the author to be well above torque values which could be applied in practice under many service conditions without the aid of power tools. If torques of a more practical value were applied, e.g. 30-40 lbf.ft (41-54 Nm) on a 16 mm dia rope, then the measured efficiencies in most cases fell dramatically below the 80% target. At these more practical torque values for 16 mm grips the efficiencies were generally below 30% and could be as low as 10%. Only the DIN 1142 grips when used as recommended at a practical torque value of 49 Nm (36 lbf.ft) gave efficiencies generally of the order of 80%.

Grease applied to the threads of the nuts or screws gave useful increases in efficiency, and in the case of the Iron grips the increase was dramatic. The greasing of the threads on every grip before assembly on a rope is a feature which might be difficult to achieve in practice, even if desirable from the performance point of view, but such an improvement in fitting technique might be adopted in some industries.

The three designs which use U bolts as part of their assembly all caused damage to the rope and fibre core at torques above about 40 lbf.ft (54 Nm). The designs which used double bridges or longer lengths of rope inside the grips were all less damaging to the rope and could have been used at higher torques than 40 lbf.ft (54 Nm) if it had been physically easier to apply such torques.

The DIN 1142 grips with smooth bridges out-performed all the designs with ridged bridges. The effects of wear on the smooth bridges was negligible. One of the reasons why the ridged bridge designs gave a poorer performance was that generally the ridges did not fit accurately into the valleys between the strands of the rope so the rope only touched the bridges on some ridge high spots. The ridges were subject to wear from pressure from the rope wires and from any movement of the rope though the grip. Ridges which were designed to fit a six strand rope would not accommodate other constructions as well.

CONCLUSIONS AND GENERAL FINDINGS FROM WHOLE PROGRAMME

Before the detailed results from this programme are discussed it must be reiterated that all the slip load tests, except the long duration tests in phase 2, were carried out using the same test rig and the same instrumentation to measure the movement. Thus the tests show the relative performance of the different permutations of BS 462 grips in a realistic manner. Similarly the relative performance of different types of grip is also realistically demonstrated.

In previous tests, where the slip points were determined by visual observation, the results were more subjective and variable between different observers. The efficiencies measured were very much higher than in these tests because slip did not become visible until its rate had reached high value. In general, termination efficiencies based on visually detected slip are appreciably higher than those calculated from the instrument detected slip initiation points as recorded in this programme. In some preliminary tests it was demonstrated that the resolution of the instrumentation was such that it detected slip at loads less than half those at which visible slip was first observed.

In addition visually detected slip is usually based on a steadily increasing load parameter, so each test lasts only a few minutes. Slip detected by the instrumentation used in this programme is based on equal increments of load applied after fixed periods of time, a much more sensitive method but one in which each test takes longer to complete.

The differences in efficiencies which arise from the two methods of detecting the slip raise important questions about how termination efficiency should be defined, especially if it is to be used in a quantitative sense in Standards, Codes of Practice, or legislation generally. Any definition must include not only the percentage of the Minimum Breaking Load (MBL) of the rope held but also the time over which it is held, and whether or not any slip movement is allowed in that period. For example, 80% termination efficiency could be defined as the ability to hold 80% of the MBL of the rope for a period of (say) 10 min with less than (say) 1 mm of slip movement after any initial elastic extension or bedding-in movement.

PHASE 1

The results from Phase 1 of the programme, which investigated the effects of different torques and different numbers of grips on the efficiency of a termination, showed clearly that if microslip movements are measured then termination efficiencies of around 80% are not practical at acceptable torque levels on ropes of 16 mm diameter with BS 462 grips of the quality being manufactured when this programme was carried out and when used in the numbers per termination recommended in the original Appendix A of BS 462:1983.

Terminations made with un-galvanised BS 462 grips gave efficiencies roughly double those made with the same number of galvanised grips when torqued up to the same value

.

To achieve 80% efficiency with un-galvanised BS 462 grips the numbers used in each termination, if torqued up to practical values, would have to be at least double the minimum numbers previously recommended in BS 462. With galvanised grips doubling the previously recommended number, if used at practical torque values, would only raise the termination efficiency to about 50%.

Greasing the U bolt threads before use with both galvanised and ungalvanised BS 462 grips produces small but useful increases in the termination efficiency Similar increases are obtained with most of the alternative designs of grip under the same circumstances.

The torques which should be applied to the nuts of BS 462 grips are much lower than the theoretical values calculated on the basis of 70% of the yield stress of the U bolt material because of the damage done to the wires, and the cores of fibre cored ropes, at the higher torques. At high torques the pressure generated under each grip causes deep nicks to form both where the wires on the strand crowns on the tail side of the rope press into the wires on the strand crowns on the live side of the rope, and where pressure from the tail side causes deep inter-strand nicking on the live side. In addition higher torques can cause stripping of the threads between the nuts and the U bolt, this damage is particularly bad with galvanised grips where larger manufacturing clearances have to be allowed to accommodate the variable thickness of the zinc coating.

Generally when fitted on fibre cored ropes there was a loss of torque on BS 462 grips of about 40% over the first few hours even when the specimens remained unloaded. The loss was appreciably less on steel cored ropes. Further losses were recorded after specimens had been loaded. Similar losses were measured on most of the alternative grips.

PHASE 2

The results from Phase 2, which investigated the loss of torque with time etc, were the least successful in this programme because the action of taking torque measurements also effectively re-torqued the nuts slightly on every occasion.

In Phase 2 a loss of torque on 16 mm BS 462 grips on a fibre cored rope of between 29% and 50% was noted over the first 24 hours when the rope was not under load. Losses of around 25% were measured within one hour in tests where the SWL of the rope was applied and held if the grips were not re-torqued at the SWL. The loss of torque on individual nuts varied very widely in many of the tests. There was no clear pattern to the loss i.e. the nuts on the grip nearest to the thimble behaved in a similar random manner to those on the grip furthest from the thimble. This loss of torque was also found on the alternative designs of grip tested. It is related to the crushing of the fibre main core. The loss of torque on steel cored ropes was appreciably less.

The tests clearly indicated the need to re-torque the nuts on BS 462 grips at intervals if the initial termination efficiency is to be maintained throughout the service life. Some recommendations on possible re-torquing intervals for passenger carrying lifting installations are given at the end of this paper.

PHASE 3

The tests on ropes of different constructions in Phase 3 showed little difference between those with fibre main cores. Only the steel cored (IWRC) rope gave higher efficiencies with BS 462 grips but only at the higher torque values used in the tests. At the more practical torque levels of around 30 lbf.ft (41 Nm) for 16 mm grips the improvement in the efficiency was very much smaller.

When the number of galvanised grips in a termination on a 16 mm dia IWRC rope was increased to five an efficiency of 80% was obtained at torques of about 40 lbf.ft (54 Nm), though it dropped to 60% at 30 lbf.ft (41 Nm). Fibre cored ropes with the same number of grips at the same torque values gave efficiencies of about 40% and 30% respectively.

PHASE 4

Tests using different sized ropes of the same construction indicated that much higher efficiencies could be achieved with terminations using BS 462 grips on small ropes, i.e. 9 mm dia. Terminations using BS 462 grips on ropes of 16 mm and 19 mm diameter had the lowest efficiencies in these tests. Tests on the other designs of grip were restricted to the 16 mm size.

Terminations using galvanised BS 462 grips, except perhaps the 9 mm and probably smaller sizes, do not give efficiencies (as measured in this programme) of the order of 80% unless either the numbers of grips used in the terminations are increased appreciably above the numbers previously recommended in the Appendices to BS 462:1958, 1969, and 1983 (before its 1985 amendment), or impractically high torque levels are used.

The torques which can be applied in practice to grips of different sizes also varies with the size. With the larger sizes there is a limitation to the physical effort which can be applied both to tighten the nuts and to hold the grip and a vice, or other clamping device, and power tools may be required. With the smaller grips the biggest problem is holding the grips for small ropes can be easily damaged by a grip twisting as it is tightened up.

PHASE 5

Although no tests were made in the main programme on BS 462 grips with smooth bridges for the reason given in Part 2, comparisons with DIN 1142 grips which had smooth bridges, suggested that the ridges in the rope groove on the bridge was not an advantageous feature and in some circumstances could be disadvantageous, especially if grips with different amounts of wear were re-used or if the grips were to be used on ropes of different constructions.

Wear on smooth bridges takes the form of a general roughening of the surface of the rope groove. Often the surface develops a texture rather like a knurled finish and this may actually add to the frictional forces opposing slip.

Where bridges had helical ridges in the rope groove it was generally found that the rope strands lay across the ridges, rather than between them, because the lay length of the rope, which varies with the tension, was different to that for which the ridges had been designed. The rope often simply lay across the ridges with contact being made at a limited number of highspots. Some of the rope grooves were also hollowed out across the bridge e.g. on the Crosby grip, the live side of the rope being pressed into the hollow by the tail side of the rope. Wear on these ridges due to wire pressure or rope slip over a period of time would be expected to have some effect, perhaps only minor, on the slip characteristics.

Tests carried out in 1992 on BS 462 grips with an improved thicker bridge indicated that the grooves in the new bridges could add about 8% to the efficiency of a three grip termination when used with the rope for which they had been designed. This increase would not apply when ropes of other constructions, or of different lay lengths, were used.

PHASE 6

Of the alternative designs of 16 mm grip tested under identical conditions the DIN 1142, Crosby, Fist and Iron grips all achieved 80% or greater efficiency in some of the tests. In most cases however the recommended torques required seem impractical to apply in most situations without the use of special tools and a rope holding device. On 16 mm rope only terminations using DIN 1142 grips appeared generally to be able to reach the 80% termination efficiency level at torque values which seemed practical to apply with conventional spanners and which caused little damage to the rope under the grips, in spite of the fact that in these tests the grips were not re-torqued after the working load had been applied as recommended in DIN 1142. Others sizes of DIN 1142 were not tested.

In tests on terminations made using the same numbers of grips at the same practical torque value the DIN 1142 grips were shown to be generally about three times more efficient than galvanised BS 462 grips. It must be repeated however that the numbers of tests carried out using these alternative designs of grips was relatively small and more tests would be needed to establish the slip v. torque characteristics accurately.

Greasing the threads of the bolts or screws in all types of grip gave useful increases in the termination efficiency.

Re-torquing the grips, immediately after installation and then at intervals throughout their service life, is essential if the initial termination efficiency is to be maintained.

It should be noted that there is another type of termination in common usage in situations where the length of the rope may need to be adjusted i.e. the "loose heart" wedge socket (e.g. Ref. BS 7166:1989 "Wedge and Socket Anchorages for Wire Ropes"). This type of termination is preferred or required in some countries, especially for passenger carrying systems. It has the advantage that it does not require regular re-torquing because the grip is provided by a wedging action which is largely self tightening. The slip performance characteristics of this type of termination were not investigated in the reported programme.

UK LEGAL REQUIREMENTS

The current UK legal requirements for the supply of wire rope grips to users for lifting purposes is covered by Section 6 of the Health and Safety at Work etc Act, 1974 as amended by the Consumer Protection Act, 1987. The amended version of Section 6 of the HSW Act is given in Schedule 3 of the Consumer Protection Act 1987. Details can also be found in the HSE leaflet IND(G)1(L)REV, "Health and Safety at Work etc Act 1974 - Articles and substances used at work -The legal duties of designers, manufacturers, importers and suppliers, and erectors and installers".

Another useful reference is the booklet "A guide to the Health and Safety at Work etc Act 1974, written by HSE and published by HMSO, 1990.

In the opinion of the author the above mentioned Acts make it clear that manufacturers, importers and suppliers of wire rope grips should provide the grip user with sufficient information to ensure the safe installation, use and maintenance of any wire rope grip termination. The grips themselves must be made to the required quality and where they claim to be made to a published Standard they must comply fully with all the material and dimensional requirements of that Standard. If a grip is made to a manufacturer's own standard, perhaps because an appropriate National or International Standard does not exist or because the manufacturer wishes to produce a higher quality product, then the manufacturer must ensure that the required quality is maintained and that the user is provided with all the information needed to ensure its safe and correct use.

RECOMMENDATIONS:

As a result of the tests carried out in this programme the author recommends that consideration should be given by wire rope grip users to the following points:

1 That DIN 1142 grips should be used in preference to BS 462 grips in all lifting situations where this type of termination is required on 16 mm diameter rope. It is probable that this recommendation could be extended to other sizes of rope but further tests might be considered necessary to confirm the performance of DIN 1142 grips on other sizes.

2 For 16 mm diameter rope the DIN recommendations with regard to the minimum number of grips to be used in terminations (i.e. 4), and the torque value (i.e. 49 Nm, 36 lbf.ft), are generally realistic and should be adhered to. Other sizes of the DIN 1142 grip were not tested.

3 If terminations using BS 462 grips, as presently made, are used for lifting then the minimum numbers of grips per termination must be increased from those originally given in Appendix A of BS 462:1958, 1969, and 1983. Where space permits consideration should be given to doubling the minimum number of grips previously recommended in BS 462. The spacing between grips must not be reduced in order to fit in extra grips.

4 To achieve maximum termination efficiency all threads and nut bearing surfaces should be greased before the grips are fitted to a rope unless the manufacturer's fitting instructions state otherwise.

5 All grips which use bolts or screws to generate the frictional grip on the rope should be re-torqued at more frequent intervals than that usually practiced, especially when used on fibre cored ropes, if the initial termination efficiency is to be maintained. The author suggests that a termination using any grip of this type on a new rope in any passenger carrying lifting application should have its grips re-torqued according to the following minimum schedule:

1. As soon as the service load is hung on the rope
2. After 24 hrs in service
3. After 7 days in service
4. After 1 month in service
5. At 6 monthly intervals from the date of installation.

In the case of lifts which operate frequently at, or near, their maximum load capacity, or lifts which are subjected to higher dynamic loading than normal, more frequent re-torquing in the first week of service would be advantageous if the maximum termination efficiency is to be maintained.

6 Where grips are used in terminations on guy and some other static ropes re-torquing at less frequent intervals would probably be acceptable and more practical. Without a re-torquing programme the efficiency of most wire rope grip terminations will gradually reduce until the integrity of the termination may be put in doubt.

7 Manufacturers of several designs of grip might usefully consider the possibility of recommending extra grips per termination, above the minimum number they currently recommend for each size of rope, so that the required torque values could be brought down to more practical values.

8 It is strongly recommended that the torque values should be measured and recorded when the terminations are made and during each subsequent inspection, especially on passenger carrying installations. This would lead to a better understanding of the reduction in torque under service conditions and help to improve maintenance procedures. This recommendation would apply not only to terminations using BS 462 grips but also to other terminations using similar types of grip, e.g. DIN 1142, Crosby, Fist, Iron, Eureka - for the different designs of grip could respond differently to service conditions and could require different maintenance schedules to compensate for the gradual compression of the rope core and the bedding-in or distortion of the strands within the grips.

9 All users of wire rope grips should ensure that they obtain from the manufacturer or supplier, and then use, full fitting and maintenance instructions for the grips. This information should include for each size of rope the minimum numbers of grips per termination, the spacing of the grips, the required initial torque settings, any requirement to grease the threads before use, and recommended re-torquing intervals for different applications. Grip manufacturers should make this information readily available to customers together with advice on how to achieve their recommended torque values if rope clamping devices and power tools are needed to reach these values safely. These instructions should also clearly state any restrictions on the use of the grips for particular types of installation.

The author wishes to acknowledge the assistance given by his colleagues in the Health and Safety Laboratory (formerly known as the Research and Laboratory Services Division, RLSD) of the Health & Safety Executive in the preparation of the test samples, the carrying out of the test programme, and in the preparation of this paper.

The views expressed in this paper are the views of the author and should not necessarily be taken to be those of the Health & Safety Executive.

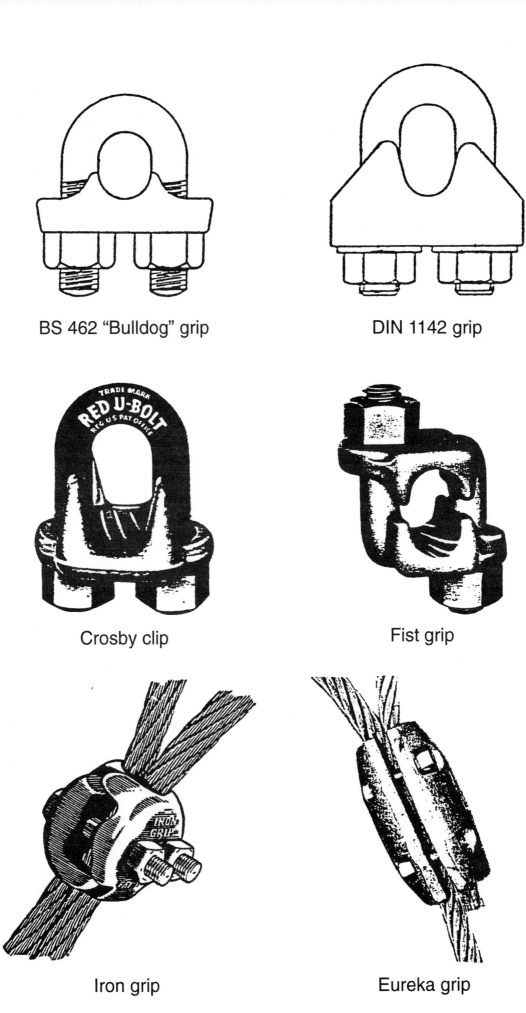

BS 462 "Bulldog" grip

DIN 1142 grip

Crosby clip

Fist grip

Iron grip

Eureka grip

Fig.20 Types of grip tested

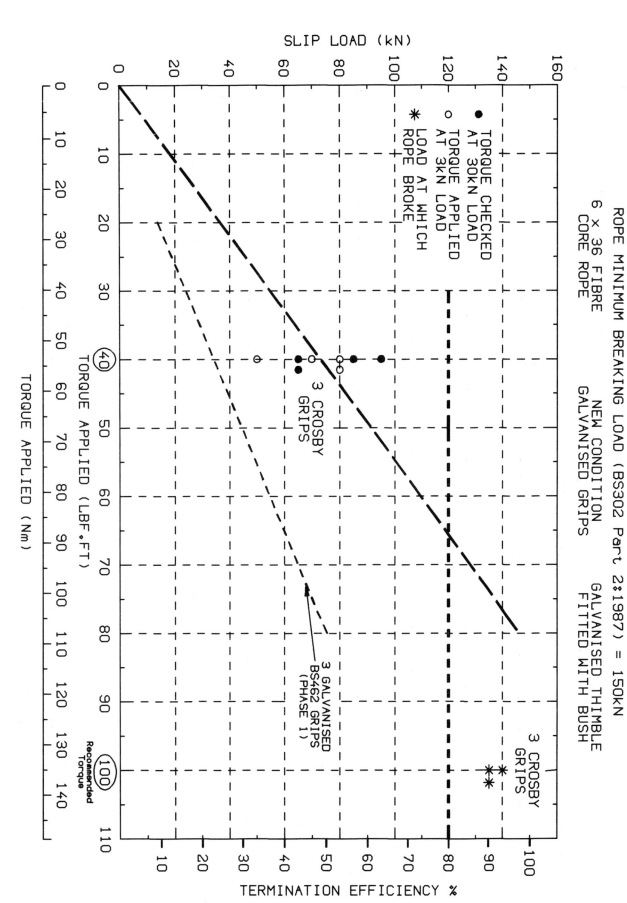

Fig.21 Crosby 3 Grip Termination Efficiency v. Initial Torque

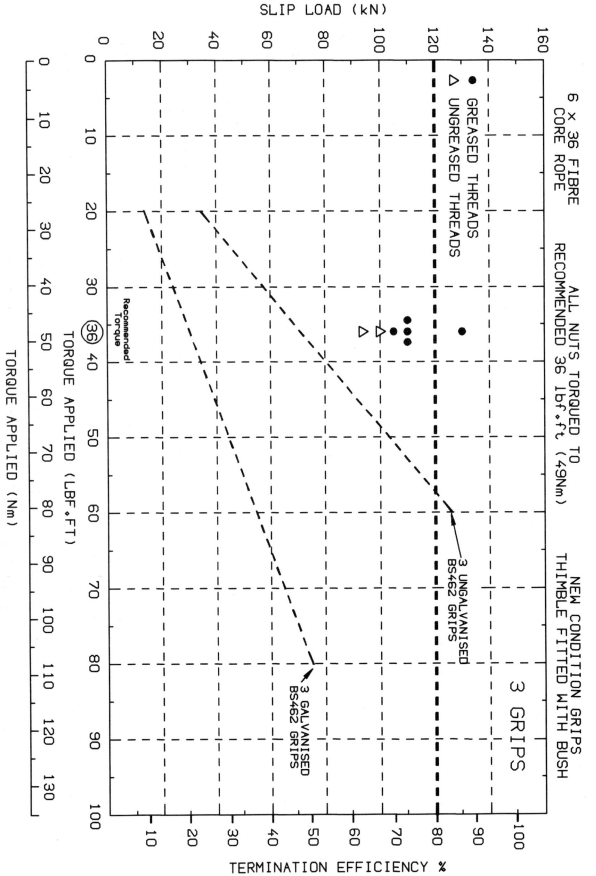

DIN 1142 16mm WIRE ROPE GRIPS

6 x 36 FIBRE
CORE ROPE

ROPE MINIMUM BREAKING LOAD (BS302 Part 2:1987) = 150kN

ALL NUTS TORQUED TO
RECOMMENDED 36 lbf.ft (49Nm)

NEW CONDITION GRIPS
THIMBLE FITTED WITH BUSH

3 GRIPS

● GREASED THREADS
△ UNGREASED THREADS

Recommended
Torque

3 UNGALVANISED
BS462 GRIPS

3 GALVANISED
BS462 GRIPS

SLIP LOAD (kN)

TORQUE APPLIED (LBF.FT)

TORQUE APPLIED (Nm)

TERMINATION EFFICIENCY %

Fig.22 DIN 3 Grip Termination Efficiency v. Initial Torque

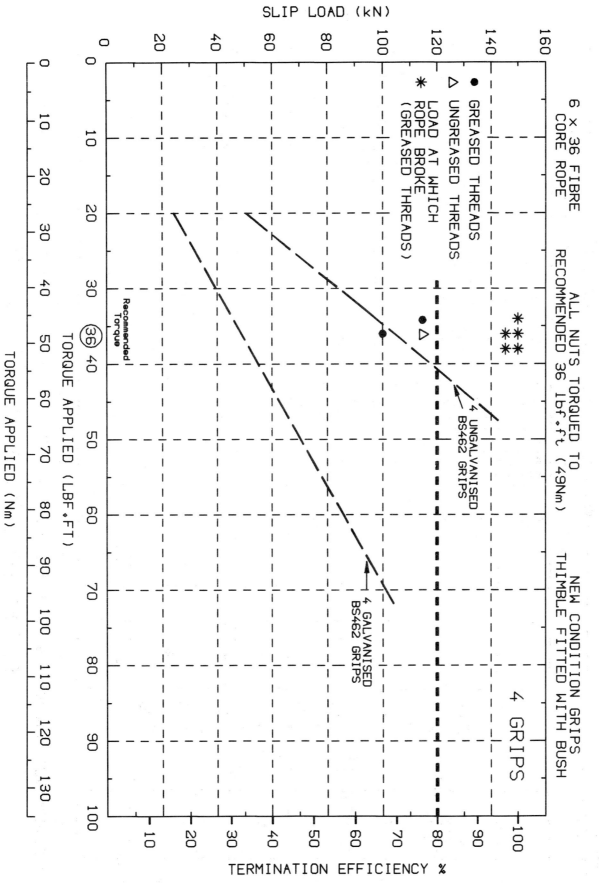

DIN 1142 16mm WIRE ROPE GRIPS

Fig.23 DIN 4 Grip Termination Efficiency v. Initial Torque

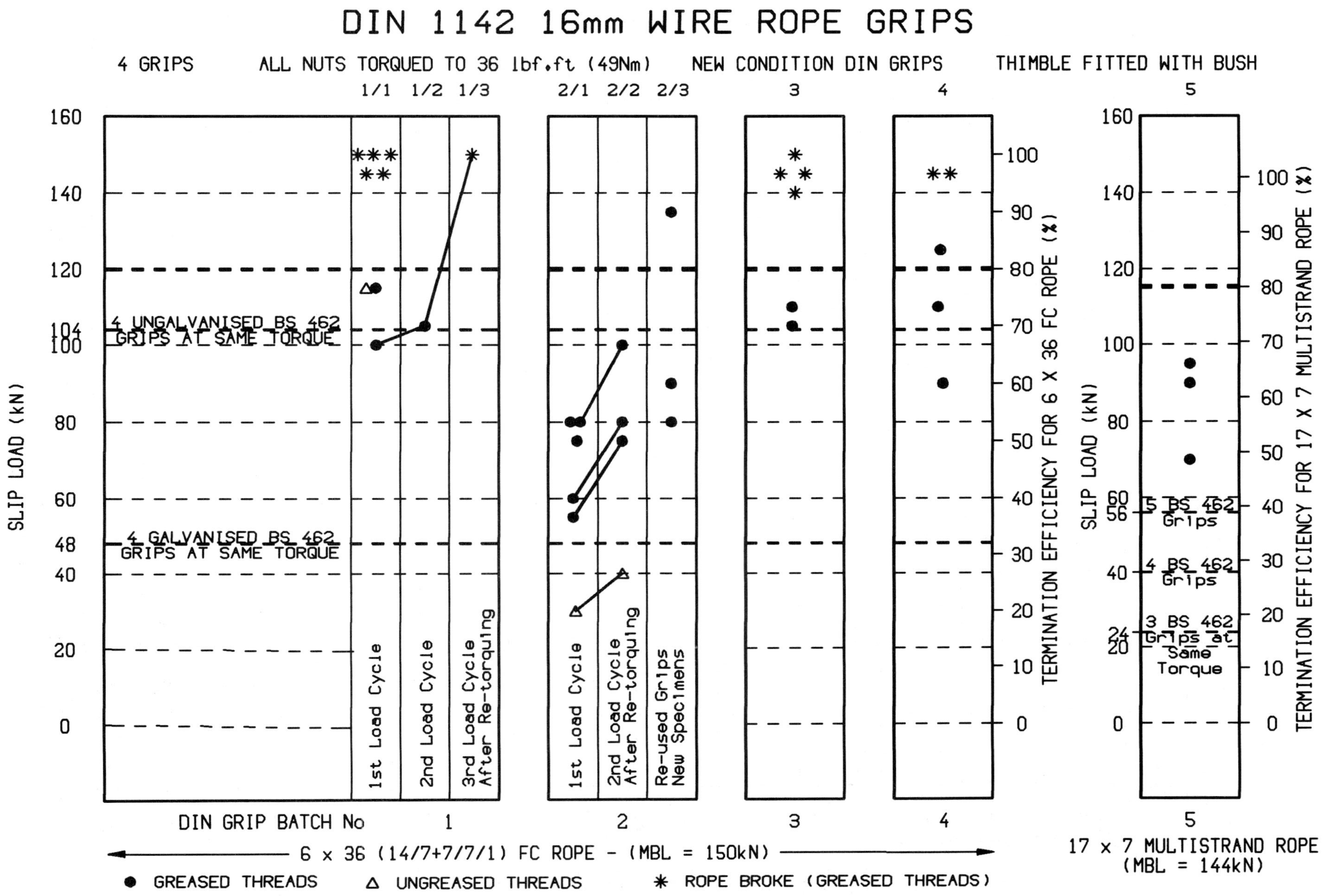

Fig.24 DIN 4 Grip Termination Efficiency with different batches of grips

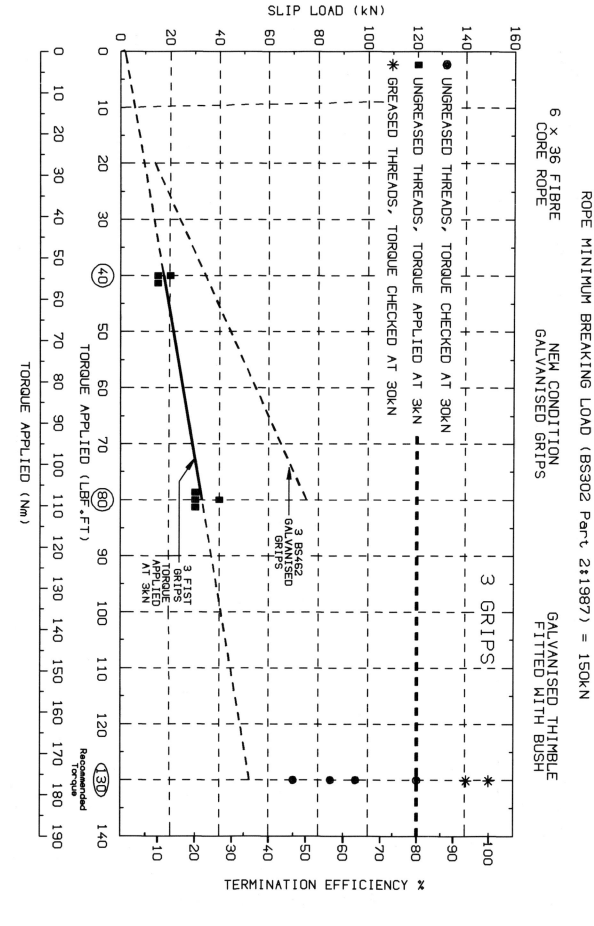

Fig.25 Fist 3 Grip Termination Efficiency v. Initial Torque

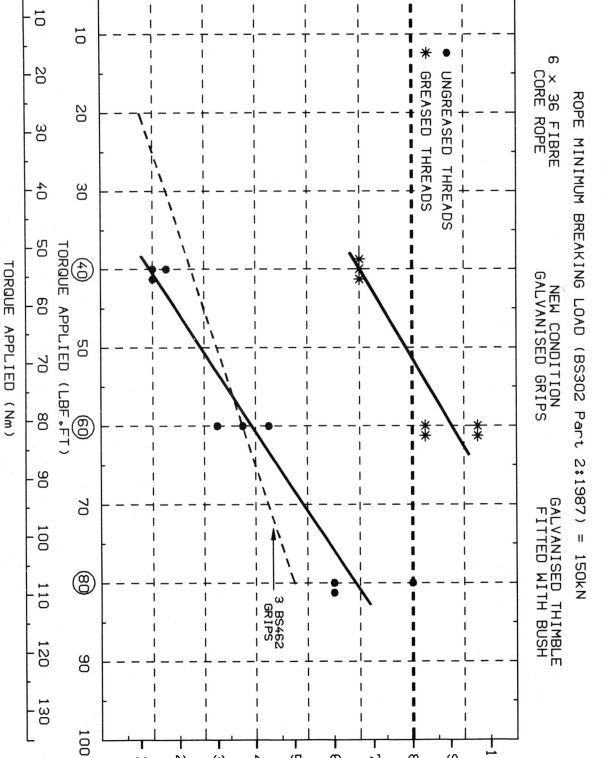

IRON 16mm WIRE ROPE GRIPS

ROPE MINIMUM BREAKING LOAD (BS302 Part 2:1987) = 150kN

6 × 36 FIBRE
CORE ROPE

NEW CONDITION
GALVANISED GRIPS

GALVANISED THIMBLE
FITTED WITH BUSH

• UNGREASED THREADS
* GREASED THREADS

3 BS462
GRIPS

SLIP LOAD (kN)

TORQUE APPLIED (LBF.FT)

TORQUE APPLIED (Nm)

TERMINATION EFFICIENCY %

Fig.26 Iron 3 Grip Termination Efficiency v. Initial Torque

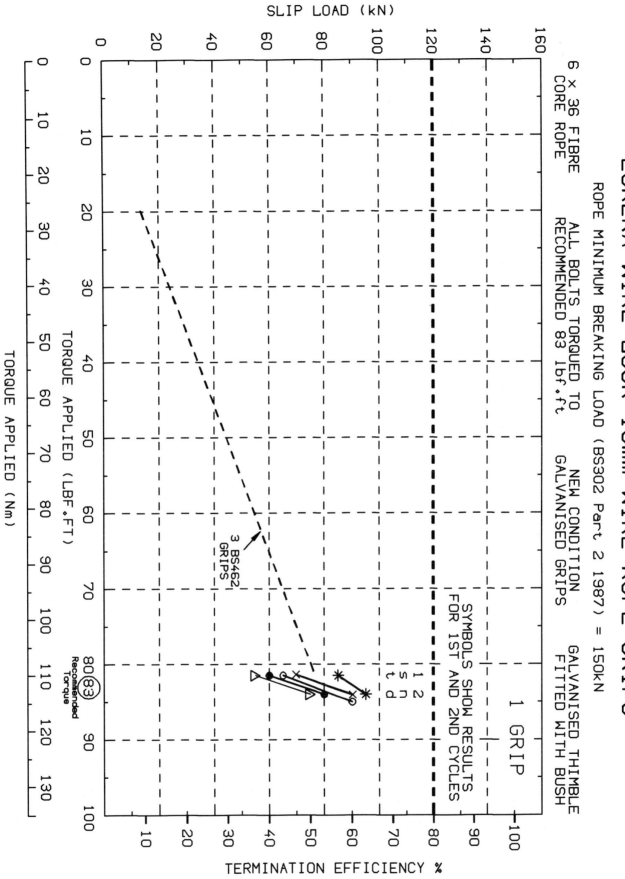

Fig.27 Eureka Grip Termination Efficiency v. Initial Torque

Printed and published by the Health and Safety Executive
C20   5/96